MW00697534

Flinn Scientific

ChemTopic™ Labs

Chemistry in the Environment

Senior Editor

Irene Cesa
Flinn Scientific, Inc.
Batavia, IL

Curriculum Advisory Board

Bob Becker
Kirkwood High School
Kirkwood, MO

Kathleen J. Dombrink
McCluer North High School
Florissant, MO

Robert Lewis
Downers Grove North High School
Downers Grove, IL

John G. Little
St. Mary's High School
Stockton, CA

Lee Marek
University of Illinois–Chicago
Chicago, IL

John Mauch
Braintree High School
Braintree, MA

Dave Tanis
Grand Valley State University
Allendale, MI

FLINN SCIENTIFIC INC.
"Your Safer Source for Science Supplies"
P.O. Box 219 • Batavia, IL 60510
1-800-452-1261 • www.flinnsci.com

ISBN 978-1-877991-92-9

Copyright © 2006 Flinn Scientific, Inc.

All rights reserved. No part of this book may be reproduced or transmitted in any form or by any means,
electronic or mechanical, including, but not limited to photocopy, recording, or any information
storage and retrieval system, without permission in writing from Flinn Scientific, Inc.
No part of this book may be included on any Web site.

Reproduction permission is granted only to the science teacher who has purchased this volume of
Flinn ChemTopic™ Labs, Chemistry in the Environment, Catalog No. AP6989 from Flinn Scientific, Inc.
Science teachers may make copies of the reproducible student pages for use only by their students.

Printed in the United States of America.

Table of Contents

Flinn ChemTopic™ Labs Series Preface
Lab Manuals Organized Around Key Content Areas in Chemistry

In conversations with chemistry teachers across the country, we have heard a common concern. Teachers are frustrated with their current lab manuals, with experiments that are poorly designed and don't teach core concepts, with procedures that are rigid and inflexible and don't work. Teachers want greater flexibility in their choice of lab activities. As we further listened to experienced master teachers who regularly lead workshops and training seminars, another theme emerged. Master teachers mostly rely on collections of experiments and demonstrations they have put together themselves over the years. Some activities have been passed on like cherished family recipe cards from one teacher to another. Others have been adapted from one format to another to take advantage of new trends in microscale equipment and procedures, technology innovations, and discovery-based learning theory. In all cases the experiments and demonstrations have been fine-tuned based on real classroom experience.

Flinn Scientific has developed a series of lab manuals based on these "cherished recipe cards" of master teachers with proven excellence in both teaching students and training teachers. Created under the direction of an Advisory Board of award-winning chemistry teachers, each lab manual in the Flinn ChemTopic™ Labs series contains 4–6 student-tested experiments that focus on essential concepts and applications in a single content area. Each lab manual also contains 4–6 demonstrations that can be used to illustrate a chemical property, reaction, or relationship and will capture your students' attention. The experiments and demonstrations in the Flinn ChemTopic™ Labs series are enjoyable, highly focused, and will give students a real sense of accomplishment.

Laboratory experiments allow students to experience chemistry by doing chemistry. Experiments have been selected to provide students with a crystal-clear understanding of chemistry concepts and encourage students to think about these concepts critically and analytically. Well-written procedures are guaranteed to work. Reproducible data tables teach students how to organize their data so it is easily analyzed. Comprehensive teacher notes include a master materials list, solution preparation guide, complete sample data, and answers to all questions. Detailed lab hints and teaching tips show you how to conduct the experiment in your lab setting and how to identify student errors and misconceptions before students are led astray.

Chemical demonstrations provide another teaching tool for seeing chemistry in action. Because they are both visual and interactive, demonstrations allow teachers to take students on a journey of observation and understanding. Demonstrations provide additional resources to develop central themes and to magnify the power of observation in the classroom. Demonstrations using discrepant events challenge student misconceptions that must be broken down before new concepts can be learned. Use demonstrations to introduce new ideas, illustrate abstract concepts that cannot be covered in lab experiments, and provide a spark of excitement that will capture student interest and attention.

Safety, flexibility, and choice

Safety always comes first. Depend on Flinn Scientific to give you upfront advice and guidance on all safety and disposal issues. Each activity begins with a description of the hazards involved and the necessary safety precautions to avoid exposure to these hazards. Additional safety, handling, and disposal information is also contained in the teacher notes.

The selection of experiments and demonstrations in each Flinn ChemTopic™ Labs manual gives you the flexibility to choose activities that match the concepts your students need to learn. No single teacher will do all of the experiments and demonstrations with a single class. Some experiments and demonstrations may be more helpful with a beginning-level class, while others may be more suitable with an honors class. All of the experiments and demonstrations have been keyed to national content standards in science education.

Chemistry is an experimental science!

Whether they are practicing key measurement skills or searching for trends in the chemical properties of substances, all students will benefit from the opportunity to discover chemistry by doing chemistry. No matter what chemistry textbook you use in the classroom, Flinn ChemTopic™ Labs will help you give your students the necessary knowledge, skills, attitudes, and values to be successful in chemistry.

About the Curriculum Advisory Board

Flinn Scientific is honored to work with an outstanding group of dedicated chemistry teachers. The members of the Flinn ChemTopic Labs Advisory Board have generously contributed their proven experiments and demonstrations to create these topic lab manuals. The wisdom, experience, creativity, and insight reflected in their lab activities guarantee that students who perform them will be more successful in learning chemistry. On behalf of all chemistry teachers, we thank the Advisory Board members for their service and dedication to chemistry education.

Bob Becker teaches chemistry and AP chemistry at Kirkwood High School in Kirkwood, MO. Bob received his B.A. from Yale University and M.Ed. from Washington University and has 20 years of teaching experience. A well-known demonstrator, Bob has conducted more than 100 demonstration workshops across the U.S. and Canada and was a Team Leader for the Flinn Foundation Summer Workshop Program. His creative and unusual demonstrations have been published in the *Journal of Chemical Education,* the *Science Teacher,* and *Chem13 News*. Bob is the author of two books of chemical demonstrations, *Twenty Demonstrations Guaranteed to Knock Your Socks Off, Volumes I and II,* published by Flinn Scientific. Bob has been awarded the James Bryant Conant Award in High School Teaching from the American Chemical Society, the Regional Catalyst Award from the Chemical Manufacturers Association, and the Tandy Technology Scholar Award.

Kathleen J. Dombrink teaches chemistry and advanced-credit college chemistry at McCluer North High School in Florissant, MO. Kathleen received her B.A. in Chemistry from Holy Names College and M.S. in Chemistry from St. Louis University and has 35 years of teaching experience. Recognized for her strong support of professional development, Kathleen has been selected to participate in the Fulbright Memorial Fund Teacher Program in Japan and NEWMAST and Dow/NSTA Workshops. She served as co-editor of the inaugural issues of *Chem Matters* and was a Woodrow Wilson National Fellowship Foundation Chemistry Team Member for 11 years. Kathleen is currently a Team Leader for the Flinn Foundation Summer Workshop Program. Kathleen has received the Presidential Award, the Midwest Regional Teaching Award from the American Chemical Society, the Tandy Technology Scholar Award, and a Regional Catalyst Award from the Chemical Manufacturers Association.

Robert Lewis retired from teaching chemistry at Downers Grove North High School in Downers Grove, IL, and is currently a Secondary Coordinator for the GATE program in Chicago. Robert received his B.A. from North Central College and M.A. from University of the South and has 30 years of teaching experience. He was a founding member of Weird Science, a group of chemistry teachers that traveled throughout the country to stimulate teacher enthusiasm for using demonstrations to teach science. Robert served as a Team Leader for both the Woodrow Wilson National Fellowship Foundation and the Flinn Foundation Summer Workshop Program. Robert has received the Presidential Award, the James Bryant Conant Award in High School Teaching from the American Chemical Society, the Tandy Technology Scholar Award, a Regional Catalyst Award from the Chemical Manufacturers Association, and a Golden Apple Award from the State of Illinois.

John G. Little teaches chemistry and AP chemistry at St. Mary's High School in Stockton, CA. John received his B.S. and M.S. in Chemistry from University of the Pacific and has 39 years of teaching experience. Highly respected for his well-designed labs, John is the author of two lab manuals, *Chemistry Microscale Laboratory Manual* (D. C. Heath), and *Microscale Experiments for General Chemistry* (with Kenneth Williamson, Houghton Mifflin). He is also a contributing author to *Science Explorer* (Prentice Hall) and *World of Chemistry* (McDougal Littell). John served as a Chemistry Team Leader for both the Woodrow Wilson National Fellowship Foundation and the Flinn Foundation Summer Workshop Program. He has been recognized for his dedicated teaching with the Tandy Technology Scholar Award and the Regional Catalyst Award from the Chemical Manufacturers Association.

Lee Marek retired from teaching chemistry at Naperville North High School in Naperville, IL and currently teaches at the University of Illinois–Chicago. Lee received his B.S. in Chemical Engineering from the University of Illinois and M.S. degrees in Physics and Chemistry from Roosevelt University. He has more than 30 years of teaching experience and is a Team Leader for the Flinn Foundation Summer Workshop Program. His students have won national recognition in the International Chemistry Olympiad, the Westinghouse Science Talent Search, and the Internet Science and Technology Fair. Lee was a founding member of Weird Science and has presented more than 500 demonstration and teaching workshops for more than 300,000 students and teachers across the country. Lee has performed science demonstrations on the *David Letterman Show* 20 times. Lee has received the Presidential Award, the James Bryant Conant Award in High School Teaching and the Helen M. Free Award for Public Outreach from the American Chemical Society, the National Catalyst Award from the Chemical Manufacturers Association, and the Tandy Technology Scholar Award.

John Mauch teaches chemistry and AP chemistry at Braintree High School in Braintree, MA. John received his B.A. in Chemistry from Whitworth College and M.A. in Curriculum and Education from Washington State University and has more than 25 years of teaching experience. John is an expert in microscale chemistry and is the author of two lab manuals, *Chemistry in Microscale, Volumes I and II* (Kendall/Hunt). He is also a dynamic and prolific demonstrator and workshop leader. John has presented the Flinn Scientific Chem Demo Extravaganza show at NSTA conventions for eight years and has conducted more than 100 workshops across the country. John was a Chemistry Team Member for the Woodrow Wilson National Fellowship Foundation program and is currently a Board Member for the Flinn Foundation Summer Workshop Program. John has received the Massachusetts Chemistry Teacher of the Year Award from the New England Institute of Chemists.

Dave Tanis is Associate Professor of Chemistry at Grand Valley State University in Allendale, MI. Dave received his B.S. in Physics and Mathematics from Calvin College and M.S. in Chemistry from Case Western Reserve University. He taught high school chemistry for 26 years before joining the staff at Grand Valley State University to direct a coalition for improving pre-college math and science education. Dave later joined the faculty at Grand Valley State University and currently teaches courses for pre-service teachers. The author of two laboratory manuals, Dave acknowledges the influence of early encounters with Hubert Alyea, Marge Gardner, Henry Heikkinen, and Bassam Shakhashiri in stimulating his long-standing interest in chemical demonstrations and experiments. Continuing this tradition of mentorship, Dave has led more than 40 one-week institutes for chemistry teachers and served as a Team Member for the Woodrow Wilson National Fellowship Foundation for 13 years. He is currently a Board Member for the Flinn Foundation Summer Workshop Program. Dave received the College Science Teacher of the Year Award from the Michigan Science Teachers Association.

Preface
Chemistry in the Environment

Earth, air, and water—these classical "elements" in ancient Greek philosophy were thought to be the basis of all living and nonliving things. Modern science has cast these "elements" in a new light. We know that the ultimate fate of our natural resources and the quality of the environment depend on physical, chemical, and biological principles and processes. Chemical reactions abound in the soil beneath our feet, the air we breathe, and the water we drink. Chemical principles provide a foundation for understanding how the soil binds nutrients, what happens to combustion gases in the atmosphere, and why lakes and streams are naturally buffered. The purpose of *Chemistry in the Environment,* Volume 22 in the Flinn ChemTopic™ Labs series, is to provide high school teachers with meaningful, easy-to-do laboratory activities that will help students apply the principles they have learned in general chemistry to chemical processes in the environment. The six experiments and five demonstrations in this book are an excellent foundation for an exciting and relevant capstone module in the science curriculum.

Chemistry and Soil Science

Soil is an essential natural resource. The physical and chemical properties of soil, including the capacity to store nutrients and the ability to protect against groundwater contamination, depend on the mixture of particles in the soil and its pH and nutrient content. In the "Physical and Chemical Properties of Soil" experiment, students analyze the composition of soil and determine soil texture, study the ability of soil to bind nutrients, and measure the pH and nutrient levels in soil. Soil is a vital component of the hydrologic (water) cycle, serving as a filter for many chemicals that may be incorporated into the soil. Chemicals that do not bind to the soil migrate through the soil and leach into the groundwater. "Cleaning Up with Iron" demonstrates a novel technological approach for removing organic pollutants from contaminated groundwater.

Chemistry and Water Quality

The amount of dissolved oxygen in water and pH are important indicators of water quality. Dissolved oxygen levels are critical in maintaining biological diversity. Use the "Dissolved Oxygen Testing" lab to organize a cooperative class project on the effect of environmental variables on the amount of oxygen dissolved in water. Students use the Winkler method to measure dissolved oxygen concentrations as a function of temperature, salinity, nutrient levels,

etc. Many lakes and streams are naturally buffered due to the presence of dissolved minerals from rocks and soil. In "pH and the Alkalinity of Water," students determine the alkalinity or buffer capacity of water by acid–base titration. Alkalinity is also closely related to water hardness—see the microscale EDTA titration in "How Hard Is Your Water?" to measure water hardness. Water purification and water cleanup activities are the focus in two demonstrations, "Clearing Water with Alum" and "Oil Spill Cleanup."

Chemistry in the Atmosphere

Gases and particulate matter released into the atmosphere as a result of both natural processes and human activities undergo a variety of photochemical and other atmospheric reactions. These reactions have a significant impact on air pollution and air quality. In "Air Pollution Investigation," students measure the amount of particulate matter in air, study the chemistry of combustion products, and explore some of the consequences of acid rain. The "Acid Rain in a Bag" demonstration is a safe microscale simulation of the properties of nitrogen oxides and the production of acid rain. A zippered bag on the overhead projector provides a model atmosphere for the generation, dispersal, and reactions of nitrogen oxides. Update your curriculum with modern developments in solar energy technology using the "Build a Solar Cell" experiment. The lab has comprehensive background information and instructions for building and testing a dye-sensitized solar cell.

Science in Personal and Social Perspectives

Building connections between the sciences and integrating social and personal perspectives are important goals of science education, and indeed these goals are formally embedded in the National Science Education Standards. The activities in *Chemistry in the Environment* offer an excellent opportunity to help students see chemistry not just in a textbook, but in the world around them. The experiments and demonstrations have been optimized to adapt them to the knowledge and skill level of the high school science curriculum, and all of the activities have been thoroughly tested and retested. You know they will work! Use the experiment summaries and concepts on the following pages to locate the concepts you want to teach and to choose experiments and demonstrations that will help you meet your goals.

Format and Features

Flinn ChemTopic™ Labs

All experiments and demonstrations in Flinn ChemTopic™ Labs are printed in a $10\frac{7}{8}'' \times 11''$ format with a wide 2″ margin on the inside of each page. This reduces the printed area of each page to a standard $8\frac{1}{2}'' \times 11''$ format suitable for copying.

The wide margin assures you the entire printed area can be easily reproduced without damaging the binding. The margin also provides a convenient place for teachers to add their own notes.

Concepts

Use these bulleted lists along with state and local standards, lesson plans, and your textbook to identify activities that will allow you to accomplish specific learning goals and objectives.

Background

A balanced source of information for students to understand why they are doing an experiment, what they are doing, and the types of questions the activity is designed to answer. This section is not meant to be exhaustive or to replace the students' textbooks, but rather to identify the core concepts that should be covered before starting the lab.

Experiment Overview

Clearly defines the purpose of each experiment and how students will achieve this goal. Performing an experiment without a purpose is like getting travel directions without knowing your destination. It doesn't work, especially if you run into a roadblock and need to take a detour!

Pre-Lab Questions

Making sure that students are prepared for lab is the single most important element of lab safety. Pre-lab questions introduce new ideas or concepts, review key calculations, and reinforce safety recommendations. The pre-lab questions may be assigned as homework in preparation for lab or they may be used as the basis of a cooperative class activity before lab.

Materials

Lists chemical names, formulas, and amounts for all reagents—along with specific glassware and equipment—needed to perform the experiment as written. The material dispensing area is a main source of student delay, congestion, and accidents. Three dispensing stations per room are optimum for a class of 24 students working in pairs. To safely substitute different items for any of the recommended materials, refer to the *Lab Hints* section in each experiment or demonstration.

Safety Precautions

Instruct and warn students of the hazards associated with the materials or procedure and give specific recommendations and precautions to protect students from these hazards. Please review this section with students before beginning each experiment.

Procedure

This section contains a stepwise, easy-to-follow procedure, where each step generally refers to one action item. Contains reminders about safety and recording data where appropriate. For inquiry-based experiments the procedure may restate the experiment objective and give general guidelines for accomplishing this goal.

Data Tables

Data tables are included for each experiment and are referred to in the procedure. These are provided for convenience and to teach students the importance of keeping their data organized in order to analyze it. To encourage more student involvement, many teachers prefer to have students prepare their own data tables. This is an excellent pre-lab preparation activity—it ensures that students have read the procedure and are prepared for lab.

Post-Lab Questions or Data Analysis

This section takes students step-by-step through what they did, what they observed, and what it means. Meaningful questions encourage analysis and promote critical thinking skills. Where students need to perform calculations or graph data to analyze the results, these steps are also laid out sequentially.

Format and Features

Teacher's Notes

Master Materials List

Lists the chemicals, glassware, and equipment needed to perform the experiment. All amounts have been calculated for a class of 30 students working in pairs. For smaller or larger class sizes or different working group sizes, please adjust the amounts proportionately.

Preparation of Solutions

Calculations and procedures are given for preparing all solutions, based on a class size of 30 students working in pairs. With the exception of particularly hazardous materials, the solution amounts generally include 10% extra to account for spillage and waste. Solution volumes may be rounded to convenient glassware sizes (100-mL, 250-mL, 500-mL, etc.).

Safety Precautions

Repeats the safety precautions given to the students and includes more detailed information relating to safety and handling of chemicals and glassware. Refers to Material Safety Data Sheets that should be available for all chemicals used in the laboratory.

Disposal

Refers to the current *Flinn Scientific Catalog/Reference Manual* for general guidelines and specific procedures governing the disposal of laboratory waste. Because we recommend that teachers review local regulations before beginning any disposal procedure, the information given in this section is for general reference purposes only. However, if a disposal step is included as part of the experimental procedure itself, then the specific solutions needed for disposal are described in this section.

Lab Hints

This section reveals common sources of student errors and misconceptions and where students are likely to need help. Identifies the recommended length of time needed to perform each experiment, suggests alternative chemicals and equipment that may be used, and reminds teachers about new techniques (filtration, pipeting, etc.) that should be reviewed prior to lab.

Teaching Tips

This section puts the experiment in perspective so that teachers can judge in more detail how and where a particular experiment will fit into their curriculum. Identifies the working assumptions about what students need to know in order to perform the experiment and answer the questions. Highlights historical background and applications-oriented information that may be of interest to students.

Sample Data

Complete, actual sample data obtained by performing the experiment exactly as written is included for each experiment. Student data will vary.

Answers to All Questions

Representative or typical answers to all questions. Includes sample calculations and graphs for all data analysis questions. Information of special interest to teachers only in this section is identified by the heading "Note to the teacher." Student answers will vary.

Look for these icons in the *Experiment Summaries and Concepts* section and in the *Teacher's Notes* of individual experiments to identify inquiry-, microscale-, and technology-based experiments, respectively.

Experiment Summaries and Concepts

Experiment

Physical and Chemical Properties of Soil—Effect on Soil Quality

Healthy soil provides structure and nutrients for plant growth and is also a vital component of the hydrologic (water) cycle. Explore how the physical and chemical properties of soil impact soil quality with this three-part investigation. Students perform settling tests to analyze the composition of soil and determine soil texture, "filter" organic dye solutions through soil to study the ability of soil to bind and store nutrients, and analyze the pH and nutrient levels in soil.

pH and the Alkalinity of Water—Buffer Capacity and Water Quality

Just as living cells contain natural buffer systems to control pH, many lakes, rivers, and streams are also naturally buffered due to the presence of dissolved minerals from soil and rocks. The purpose of this experiment is to analyze the buffering capacity or alkalinity of water by titration with a standard hydrochloric acid solution to a methyl orange endpoint. Alkalinity is expressed in terms of parts per million calcium carbonate.

How Hard Is Your Water?—Microscale Titration

As water flows through rocks and soil, it picks up minerals from the Earth's surface. High levels of minerals such as calcium, magnesium, and iron ions create "hard water" and are often a nuisance. The purpose of this experiment is to analyze water hardness by microscale titration with EDTA. Water hardness levels are determined using a standard graph obtained by plotting the number of drops of EDTA versus water hardness for a set of standard solutions.

Air Pollution Investigation—Air Quality

How clean is the air you breathe? How does the air look, taste, smell or feel? Investigate the origin and types of air pollution with this three-part laboratory activity. Students measure the amount of particulate matter in air by "capturing" the particles on microscope slides, learn how combustion products contribute to air pollution and air quality, and examine the effects of acid rain on common building materials and living organisms.

Build a Solar Cell—Photovoltaic Effect and Photosynthesis

Update your curriculum today—build a dye-sensitized solar cell with your students! The solar cell consists of conductive glass plates containing titanium oxide (a semiconductor) at the anode, and graphite at the cathode. The titanium oxide is coated with a natural dye that absorbs visible light. Light striking the dye surface excites an electron, which enters the conduction band and travels through the external circuit, producing electricity from light.

Dissolved Oxygen Testing—Biochemical Oxygen Demand and Water Quality

Dissolved oxygen is one of the best indicators of water quality. Organize a cooperative class project to investigate the effects of environmental conditions on the amount of oxygen dissolved in water. Dissolved oxygen levels are measured in the laboratory using the Winkler method. Variables that may be studied include temperature, concentration of sodium chloride or dissolved nutrients, and biochemical oxygen demand.

Concepts

- Soil quality and soil texture
- Cation exchange capacity
- Acids, bases, and pH
- Nitrates and phosphates

- Acids, bases, and pH
- Alkalinity
- Buffers and buffer capacity
- Acid rain and water pollution

- Water hardness
- EDTA titration
- Chelates and complex ions
- Water softening

- Air pollution and air quality
- Particulates in air
- Combustion products
- Acid rain

- Solar energy
- Photovoltaic cell
- Photoelectric effect
- Semiconductors

- Dissolved oxygen
- Winkler method
- Biological oxygen demand
- Water quality

Experiment Summaries and Concepts

Demonstration

Concepts

Clearing Water with Alum—Water Purification

Where does drinking water come from and how is it purified? Most of the suspended solids in water consist of small, dispersed particles that cannot be separated by filtration. In this demonstration, a commercial purification procedure for removing suspended solids from drinking water is introduced. Adding alum causes the colloidal particles to coagulate and "settle down."

- Coagulation
- Flocculant
- Water purification

Acid Rain in a Bag—Reaction of Nitrogen Oxides in the Atmosphere

Perform a safe, microscale simulation of acid rain formation. A zippered bag on the overhead projector is a model atmosphere for the generation, dispersal, and reactions of nitrogen oxides with air and water. Observe a brown cloud of nitrogen dioxide safely contained within the bag, and follow the acid–base indicator color changes to see how acid rain is formed.

- Oxidation–reduction
- Acid–base indicators
- Acid rain

Buffering of Lakes and Streams—Acid Neutralization in Nature

An "acid rainfall" solution is poured through a column of marble chips to illustrate the formation of a buffer in lakes with a limestone bed. Observe the rainbow spectrum of color changes as acid rain containing universal indicator slowly filters through the calcium carbonate "rocks," and then test the ability of the resulting "lake" or filtrate to neutralize additional acid rain.

- Acid rain
- Acid–base indicators
- Buffers

Oil Spill Cleanup—Detergents, Dispersants, and Polymers

Model an oil spill and let students explore possible solutions to the problems that arise because oil and water do not mix. The demonstration includes the use of commercial polymer technology for cleaning up oil and fuel spills. The unique absorbent polymer bonds quickly and safely to liquid hydrocarbons, generating a solid waste product that separates from the water and is easily removed.

- Oil spills
- Detergents and dispersants
- Absorbent polymers

Cleaning Up with Iron—Redox Reactions and Groundwater Remediation

Permeable reactive barriers (PRBs) are walls built below ground to remove pollutants from contaminated groundwater. PRBs made of metallic iron are used to remove chlorinated organic compounds from groundwater. Iron is a good reducing agent—it reduces toxic organic compounds and converts them to less harmful substances. The reaction of iron powder with organic redox indicators demonstrates the "potential" of this method for cleaning up organic pollutants.

- Groundwater remediation
- Permeable reactive barriers
- Oxidation–reduction

Teacher Notes

Physical and Chemical Properties of Soil
Effect on Soil Quality

Introduction

In 1937, in the aftermath of the tragic "Dust Bowl," President Roosevelt wrote to the nation's governors about the importance of soil quality and soil conservation. "The nation that destroys its soil destroys itself," Roosevelt said, urging the states to adopt strict soil conservation measures. How do the physical and chemical properties of soil affect soil quality?

Concepts

- Soil quality and soil texture
- Cation exchange capacity
- Acids, bases, and pH
- Nitrates and phosphates

Background

Soil is an important natural resource. By providing both structure and nutrients for plant growth, healthy soil ensures a bountiful and healthy food supply for life on Earth. Soil is also a vital component of the hydrologic (water) cycle. Soil acts as a natural filter, adsorbing chemicals that may be applied to the soil or incorporated into the soil from other sources. "Chemical waste" that may be processed by the soil includes fertilizers, herbicides and pesticides, biological and agricultural waste products, and industrial waste chemicals. The ability of soil to protect against runoff and groundwater contamination depends on the mixture of particles in the soil, its pH and oxygen content, the amount of organic matter, and on the presence of microorganisms.

Often thought of as "just dirt," soil is actually a complex mixture of inorganic minerals and organic matter, as well as air, water, and even biological organisms. As a rough estimate, only about 50% of soil consists of "solids" (inorganic and organic substances)—the rest is air and water. The physical properties of soil depend on the mixture and size distribution of mineral particles making up the soil. The USDA classifies *soil particles* into three categories based on their grain size: sand, silt, and clay. See Table 1.

Table 1. USDA Classification of Soil Particles

Particle	Clay	Silt	Sand
Size	<0.002 mm	0.002 mm–0.05 mm	0.05 mm–2 mm

Soil texture describes the relative amounts of sand, silt, and clay in a mass of soil—it is one of the most important indicators of soil quality. The texture of soil determines how coarse or fine the soil is, its porosity and permeability, and the capacity to store nutrients and bind waste products. Sandy soils have excellent drainage and lots of air spaces, but they do not bind nutrients or support root growth. Sandy soils feel dry and gritty, and nutrients leach out quickly. Clay soils, on the other hand, consist of microscopic particles that clump together and retain water. Soils with high clay content are easily waterlogged and have a tendency to exclude air and become anaerobic, killing off the living organisms that are a necessary part of healthy soil. Clay has a large surface area, however, and is chemically very active, binding and storing both mineral and organic nutrients. The most productive soils

Soil is not a simply defined substance. The layers of soil composing the Earth's surface are constantly being altered by landscape, climate, vegetation, and the action of living organisms. Different types of soil are grouped into classes, called soil series, based on their composition and physical and chemical properties. The Department of Agriculture (USDA) has identified more than 15,000 soil series in the United States!

have a balance of sand, silt, and clay and are called loams or loamy soils. ("Rich" soils also contain high concentrations of organic matter.)

The USDA has identified 12 main textural classes of soil based on the percentage of clay, sand, and silt. The textural class is determined using a three-sided graph called the *soil texture triangle* (Figure 1). Each side of the triangle represents one of the *soil separates* on a scale from 0 to 100%. The graph is read by following the clay percent line parallel to the triangle base, the sand line parallel to the right side of the triangle, and the silt line parallel to the left side of the triangle. Follow the arrows in Figure 1: A soil containing 30% clay, 50% sand, and 20% silt is classified as *sandy clay loam*.

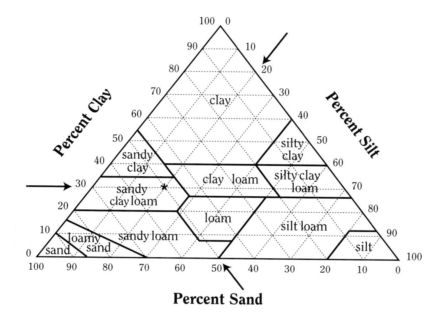

Figure 1. Soil Texture Triangle.

One of the most important functions of soil is to store essential nutrients and exchange them with plants through their roots. This function is largely provided by the clay minerals in soil and by organic compounds (humus) originating from the decay of living organisms. Clay consists of negatively charged, colloidal particles that selectively adsorb positively charged cations. The ability of soil to bind cations is called its *cation-exchange capacity* or CEC. Cation exchange provides the mechanism for the uptake of potassium, calcium, magnesium, and other trace metals by plants. Metal cations delivered to the plants in this way are replaced by hydrogen ions from the roots of the plant. CEC depends on the acid–base properties of soil—most common plants grow best in neutral soils.

The pH of soil indicates whether the soil is acidic or basic. The pH scale is defined from 0 (very acidic) to 14 (highly basic). pH 7 is neutral, pH >7 is basic, and pH <7 is acidic (Figure 2). Soil pH influences the solubility and availability of soil nutrients, the viability of essential microorganisms, and the movement of toxic heavy metals into groundwater. A pH range between 6 and 7 is ideal for most plants. When soil is too acidic (<5.6), the plants cannot utilize the nutrients they need, and excessive amounts of aluminum and iron, which are harmful to plants, dissolve into the soil solution.

Teacher Notes

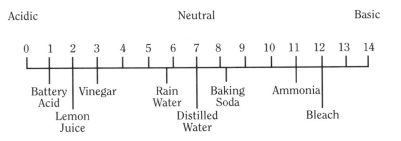

Figure 2. The pH Scale.

The elements C, H, O, N, P, K, Ca, Mg, and S are considered *macronutrients* because plants need them in large amounts. Of these, C, H, and O come from the atmosphere and Ca, Mg, and S come from the mineral content in the Earth. The nutrients that are most likely to be missing are N, P, and K—these elements are commonly added to soils in the form of fertilizers. Nitrate ions are the most common source of nitrogen for plants. Before the widespread use of nitrogen fertilizers, soil nitrogen was primarily provided by legumes (soybeans, alfalfa, and clover). The root structures of legumes contain bacteria that are capable of converting nitrogen from the air into ammonia and nitrate ions. Nitrogen is an essential component of proteins—plants grown in nitrogen-rich soils provide higher yields and are richer in protein and therefore more nutritious. Nitrogen is also needed to produce healthy leaf growth and green leaves. Phosphorus, which occurs naturally in soil in the form of phosphate minerals, is important for root growth and also aids in the production of flowers and fruit. Adequate levels of phosphorus (2–4 ppm) are especially important for root crops (beets, potatoes, carrots, radishes, etc.). In addition to fertilizers, other sources of nitrates and phosphates in soil include decaying vegetation, human and animal waste products, and industrial waste discharge.

Nitrate and phosphate pollution of surface water and groundwater is a major problem in many areas. Nitrate ions do not bind to soil particles and are thus readily leached into groundwater. Unpolluted water generally contains less than 4 parts per million (ppm) nitrate. When the concentration of nitrate ions exceeds 10 ppm, water may be unfit to drink. High levels of phosphate accumulate in the top layers of soil in the form of insoluble calcium phosphate—subsequent runoff and erosion produces phosphate-rich sediments in surface water. Nitrate and phosphate pollution leads to the overgrowth of algae and other organisms (algae blooms), which deplete the water of oxygen and kill off fish.

Experiment Overview

The purpose of this experiment is to investigate the physical and chemical properties of soil. There are three parts to the experiment:

Part A. Soil texture will be determined by measuring the heights of the sand, silt, and clay layers at appropriate time intervals after mixing soil with "softened" water. The rate at which soil particles settle when mixed with water depends on their size. Large sand particles settle out quickly, within 1 minute, silt particles generally settle within 30 minutes, while tiny clay particles may take up to 24 hours. Dividing the height of the respective soil layer by the combined height of all three layers gives the percentage of each component. The "softening agent" is Calgon (sodium hexametaphosphate), which causes the colloidal clay particles to clump together and "settle down."

Part B. The ability of soil to bind and store nutrients or other environmental chemicals will be studied by "filtering" organic dye solutions through soil and sand. Two dyes will be compared: methylene blue, which has a positive charge, and eosin Y, which has a negative charge.

Part C. The chemical properties of soil will be evaluated by measuring the pH and testing for the presence of macronutrients. The levels of these soil quality indicators are determined by mixing the soil with water and analyzing the resulting solutions.

Pre-Lab Questions

1. Draw a circle about 4 cm in diameter to represent the maximum size of a sand particle. Using the dimensions of soil particles summarized in Table 1, draw two smaller circles to scale within this circle to represent the relative sizes of silt and clay particles, respectively.

2. Consider the overall picture of the soil texture triangle (Figure 1). Which soil component seems to have the largest influence in determining the properties of a class of soil? Explain.

3. A soil was analyzed using the method described in Part A of this activity. The heights of the sand, silt, and clay layers were 6 mm, 8 mm, and 6 mm, respectively. Calculate the percentage of each component and identify the soil textural class using the soil texture triangle.

Materials

Calgon solution, 5%, 1 mL

Eosin Y solution, 0.2%, 40 mL

Methylene blue solution, 0.2%, 40 mL

Sand, fine, 40 cm^3

Soil, about 60 cm^3 (75 g), air-dried

Vinegar (acetic acid solution), CH_3CO_2H, 2 mL

Nitrate TesTab® tablet or Rapitest® capsule

pH TesTab® tablet or pH paper, narrow range, pH 6.0–8.0

Phosphate TesTab® tablet or Rapitest® capsule

Rubber stoppers, to fit test tubes (size 1), 3

Test tubes, 16 × 125 mm, 5

Test tube rack

Color comparison charts for pH, phosphate, and nitrate tests

Beakers, 50-mL, or small cups, 6

Beral pipets, 5

Buret clamps, 4

Glass wool or cotton ball

Graduated cylinder, 10- or 25-mL

Metric ruler

Permanent marker

Ring (support) stands, 2

Spatulas or plastic spoons, 2

Syringes, plastic (without needles), 35- or 60-mL, 4

Timer or watch

Vial, plastic, Snap-Seal™, 45-mL

Wash bottle and distilled water

Safety Precautions

TesTab® tablets or Rapitest® capsules contain small amounts of chemicals that may irritate skin. Please observe all normal laboratory safety guidelines. Wear goggles or safety glasses whenever working chemicals, heat or glassware in the laboratory. Do not handle soil with bare hands. Wash hands thoroughly with soap and water before leaving the lab.

Teacher Notes

Procedure

1. Form a working group with three other students and work together on Part A. One pair of students should then do Part B while the second pair works on Part C. Share data at the conclusion of the experiment.

Part A. Soil Texture

2. Using a spatula, add about 10 cm³ of air-dried soil to a plastic, Snap-Seal™ vial. Gently tap the vial on the table or countertop to eliminate air spaces and pack the soil down in the tube.

3. Carefully add distilled water to the vial until the water level is at the 40-mL line.

4. Using a graduated, Beral-type pipet, add 1 mL of Calgon solution to the vial.

5. Cap the vial and snap securely to prevent leakage. Shake vigorously for two minutes to thoroughly mix the contents of the vial.

6. Place the vial on the countertop and *immediately start timing.* (Set the vial down in a convenient place where you will be able to observe and measure the soil layers but where the vial will not be disturbed for 24 hours. Do not jostle or move the vial!)

7. *After exactly one minute,* measure the height in mm of the *sand layer* that has settled to the bottom of the vial. Record the measurement in the data table.

8. After 30 minutes, measure and record the *combined height* in mm of the sand and silt layers.

9. After 24 hours, measure and record the total height of the clay, sand, and silt layers. Record the color and appearance of the water solution on top of the soil. *Note:* The clay will probably look "congealed" and is usually lighter in color than the other layers.

Part B. Dye Filtration

10. Obtain four large syringes (set the plungers aside—they will not be used).

11. Place a *small* piece of glass wool or cotton in the bottom of each syringe (barrel) to cover the opening.

12. Add approximately 20 cm³ of *air-dried soil* to two syringes and lightly tap the syringes to pack the soil samples (Figure 3).

13. Add approximately 20 cm³ of fine *sand* to the remaining two syringes.

14. Clamp each syringe, tip down, to a support stand, and place a small beaker, flask, or cup under each syringe.

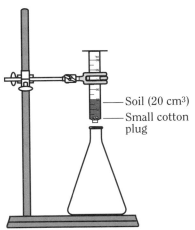

Soil (20 cm³)
Small cotton plug

Figure 3.

15. Obtain 20 mL of *methylene blue* solution in a small cup and slowly add the dye to the *soil* in one of the syringes. Allow the dye solution to pass through the soil "filter" and collect the filtrate in the beaker or flask.

16. Obtain 20 mL of *eosin Y (eosin red)* solution in a small cup and slowly add the dye to the soil in the second syringe. Allow the dye solution to pass through the soil "filter" and collect the filtrate in the beaker or flask.

17. Repeat steps 15 and 16 using the syringes filled with *sand*.

18. Record the *volume* and *color* of each filtrate in the data table.

Part C. Chemical Properties of Soil

19. Obtain TesTabs® or other pre-packaged pH, nitrate, and phosphate tablets or capsules for soil testing. *Note:* The following directions are for the use of TesTab tablets. Follow the instructions on the soil testing kit for the actual products used.

20. Mark the 1-mL and 10-mL levels in each test tube: Measure 1 mL of water in a graduated cylinder and add the water to one of the test tubes. Using a permanent marker, draw a line on the test tube to mark the 1-mL level. Add 9 mL water to the test tube and draw a second line to mark the 10-mL level. Hold two test tubes side-by-side with the marked test tube and draw lines for the 1-mL and 10-mL levels on each. Discard the water.

21. Using a clean spatula or plastic spoon, add soil to the 1-mL level in each test tube and label the test tubes pH, N, and P.

22. Add distilled water to the 10-mL mark in the *pH test tube*. If using narrow-range pH paper to test the pH, skip step 23 and proceed directly to step 24.

23. Add a pH TesTab tablet to the water in the pH test tube.

24. Stopper the test tube and shake vigorously for 30 seconds. Place the test tube in a test tube rack and allow 2–3 minutes for the soil to settle.

25. Compare the color of the liquid in the pH test tube to the colors on the pH Color Comparison Chart. Record the approximate pH value in the data table. *Optional:* If using pH paper, place a drop of the liquid on the pH paper. Match the resulting color to the color chart and record the pH in the data table.

26. Using a graduated Beral pipet, add 1 mL of vinegar to both the *N and P test tubes*.

27. Add distilled water to the *N and P test tubes* until the liquid level in each is at the 10-mL mark. Stopper the test tubes and shake vigorously for one minute each.

28. Place the test tubes in a test tube rack and allow 3–5 minutes for the soil to settle.

29. Decant 5 mL of liquid from the *N test tube* into a clean test tube and add a Nitrate TesTab tablet to the clear liquid. Stopper the test tube and shake vigorously for at least one minute or until the tablet dissolves.

30. Place the test tube in a test tube rack and let it sit undisturbed for 5 minutes. Compare the color of the liquid to the colors on the Nitrate Color Comparison Chart. Record the nitrate concentration in the data table.

31. Repeat steps 29 and 30 with the P test tube, using a Phosphate TesTab tablet and the Phosphate Color Comparison Chart. Record the phosphate concentration in the data table.

Teacher Notes

Name: _____

Class/Lab Period: _____

Physical and Chemical Properties of Soil

Data Table

Part A. Soil Texture			
Soil Particle Layer	**Sand (1 minute)**	**Sand + Silt (30 minutes)**	**Sand + Silt + Clay (24 hours)**
Height			
Color and appearance of water solution			

Part B. Dye Filtration			
Dye	**Filter Material**	**Color of Filtrate**	**Volume of Filtrate**
Methylene Blue	Soil		
	Sand		
Eosin Y	Soil		
	Sand		

Part C. Chemical Properties			
Test	**pH**	**Nitrate**	**Phosphate**
Level or concentration			

Post-Lab Questions

1. *(a)* Calculate the *percentages* of sand, silt, and clay in the soil sample: Divide the height of each respective soil layer by the combined height of all three layers, and multiply by 100.

   (b) Identify the soil texture class using the *soil texture triangle* (Figure 1).

2. Compare and contrast the results of the dye filtration experiment:
   (a) Which dye was retained (adsorbed) by the soil sample? How do you know?
   (b) Explain why one dye was retained by the soil while the other dye moved through the soil.
   (c) What was the purpose of including sand in the design of this experiment?

3. Use the chemical test results from Part C to describe the soil quality:
   (a) Is the soil acidic or basic?
   (b) Are the levels of nitrates and phosphates suitable for plant growth? Explain.
   (c) Would you recommend that a fertilizer be applied to the soil before the next growing season? Why or why not?

4. Which type of soil particle has the largest *surface area* (surface-to-volume ratio)? How does this characteristic influence the physical and chemical properties of soil? Explain.

5. Explain why the pH of soil is an important aspect of soil fertility.

6. Most state departments of agriculture recommend that farmers test their soil every year before applying fertilizers. What are the economic benefits of soil testing for the farmer? What are the general environmental benefits of soil testing?

7. Describe the primary functions of nitrogen and phosphorus for plant growth. What are some natural sources of nitrates and phosphates in the soil?

8. How do excess nitrates and phosphates from the soil end up in groundwater or surface water, respectively? Why is this a problem?

Teacher's Notes
Physical and Chemical Properties of Soil

Master Materials List *(for a class of 28 students working in groups of four)*

Calgon™ solution, 5%, 10 mL	Beakers, 50-mL, or small cups, 42
Eosin Y solution, 0.2%, 300 mL	Beral pipets, 35
Methylene blue solution, 0.2%, 300 mL	Buret clamps, 28
Sand, fine, 300 cm³	Glass wool or cotton balls
Soil, about 500 cm³ (625 g), air-dried	Graduated cylinders, 10- or 25-mL, 7
Vinegar (acetic acid solution), CH_3CO_2H, 20 mL	Metric rulers, 7
Nitrate TesTab® tablets or Rapitest® capsules, 7	Permanent markers, 7
pH TesTab® tablets, 7, or pH paper, narrow range, pH 6.0–8.0	Ring (support) stands, 14
	Spatulas or plastic spoons, 14
Phosphate TesTab® tablets or Rapitest® capsules, 7	Syringes, plastic (without needles), 35- or 60-mL, 28
Rubber stoppers, to fit test tubes (size 1), 21	
Test tubes, 16 × 125 mm, 35	Timers or watches, 7
Test tube racks, 7	Vials, plastic, Snap-Seal™, 45-mL, 7
Color comparison charts for pH, phosphate, and nitrate tests*	Wash bottles and distilled water, 7

*See the Lab Hints section.

Preparation of Solutions *(for a class of 28 students working in groups of four)*

Calgon Solution, 5%: Weigh 1.0 g of Calgon™ water softening agent (powder) in a beaker or flask and add 20 mL of distilled or deionized water. Stir to dissolve and mix well.

Eosin Y, 0.2%: Weigh 1.0 g of Eosin Y indicator dye in a beaker or flask and add 500 mL of distilled or deionized water. Stir to dissolve and mix well.

Methylene Blue, 0.2%: Weigh 1.0 g of methylene blue indicator in a beaker or flask and add 500 mL of 95% ethyl alcohol. Stir to dissolve and mix well.

Safety Precautions

TesTab® tablets or Rapitest® capsules contain small amounts of chemicals that may irritate the skin. Please observe all normal laboratory safety guidelines. Wear goggles or safety glasses whenever working chemicals, heat or glassware in the laboratory. Do not handle soil with bare hands. Please review current Material Safety Data Sheets for additional safety, handling, and disposal information. Remind students to wash hands thoroughly with soap and water before leaving the lab.

Disposal

Please consult your current *Flinn Scientific Catalog/Reference Manual* for general guidelines and specific procedures governing the disposal of laboratory waste. The dye solutions may be disposed of down the drain with plenty of excess water according to Flinn Suggested Disposal Method #26b.

Lab Hints

- For best results, schedule at least two 50-minute lab periods for completion of this activity. This should allow plenty of time both to review the background material and *Pre-Lab Questions* and also to discuss the results.

- Encourage students to bring in soil samples for study. To make the soils easier to handle, dry the samples in air for 1–2 days prior to testing—simply spread out the soil on packing paper or newspaper and allow to dry.

- Snap-Seal vials are excellent sampling containers for field studies and are ideal for the soil texture experiment. The vials are made of chemically resistant polypropylene and have secure seals that will not leak. The vials also have uniform diameters and permanent volume graduations in milliliters. Many other containers may also be used—select containers that are relatively tall and narrow and have uniform diameter. Use a 1:3 ratio of soil to water, and leave an air space above the soil–water mixture.

- Soils with high clay content may not settle well, even after 24 hours—the "soil solution" will remain dark brown and cloudy. In general, adding more Calgon (about 5 mL) to clay soils will improve the settling, but the clay tends to become incorporated into the silt layer and may not be visible as a separate layer. For accurate results, the amount of clay suspended in the solution can be determined based upon density using a hydrometer.

- Some settling tests involve measuring the initial height (A) of the air-dried soil before adding water and Calgon, measuring the total settled height after 1 minute (B) and 30 minutes (C), respectively, and then using the difference to calculate the height of clay (Clay = A − C). [Percent silt = (C − B)/A, etc.] In our experience, the total settled height after 30 minutes was *always* greater than the initial height of the air-dried soil, giving "negative" percentages for the amount of clay.

- The structures of methylene blue, an organic redox dye, and eosin Y, a fluorescent biological indicator stain, are shown below. Methylene blue is blue in its oxidized form, and the chromophore (colored part of the structure) is positively charged. Eosin Y, which is red but has a strong green fluorescence, is used to stain plasma. The chromophore is negatively charged (anionic).

Methylene Blue   *Eosin Y*

- TesTab tablets are versatile, single-factor test tablets for a wide range of analytes. They may be used for either water or soil analysis. Pre-packaged soil testing kits may also be purchased at nurseries, home and garden centers, and hardware stores. (These products generally come with their own unique branded color comparison charts or systems.)

Flinn Scientific carries a complete line of TesTab products for soil and water testing. Look under Water Investigation Kits in the Earth Science section of the Flinn Scientific Catalog/Reference Manual.

Teacher Notes

Teaching Tips

- See the *Supplementary Information* section for a standard procedure and sample data for determining the organic content in soil.

- Consult soil surveys (maps of soil texture) to obtain more information about soil types and soil texture across the country. Interactive maps of soil texture, pH, porosity, permeability, bulk density, etc. are available at the following Web sites:

  http://www.soilinfo.psu.edu/index.cgi?soil_data&conus&data_cov (Earth System Science Center at Pennsylvania State University)

  http://websoilsurvey.nrcs.usda.gov/app/ (Natural Resources Conservation Service)

Answers to Pre-Lab Questions *(Student answers will vary.)*

1. Draw a circle about 4 cm in diameter to represent the maximum size of a sand particle. Using the dimensions of soil particles summarized in Table 1, draw two smaller circles to scale within this circle to represent the relative sizes of silt and clay particles, respectively.

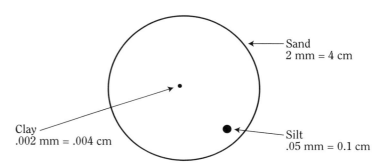

2. Consider the overall picture of the soil texture triangle (Figure 1). Which soil component seems to have the largest influence in determining the properties of a class of soil? Explain.

   Clay seems to have the largest effect on the properties of soil—almost the entire top one-half portion of the soil texture triangle is dominated by clay. With few exceptions, any soil containing more than 40% clay is simply classified as "clay." The properties of clay that cause it to dominate the soil texture triangle include its capacity to hold water and its tendency to become waterlogged, and its ability to bind nutrients and other chemicals.

3. A soil was analyzed using the method described in Part A of this activity. The heights of the sand, silt, and clay layers were 6 mm, 8 mm, and 6 mm, respectively. Calculate the percentage of each component and identify the soil textural class using the soil texture triangle.

   Total soil height = (6 + 8 + 6) mm = 20 mm

   Percent sand = (6/20) × 100% = 30%

   Percent silt = (8/20) × 100% = 40%

   Percent clay = 30%

   *Soil containing 30% sand, 40% silt, and 30% clay is classified as a **clay loam**.*

Sample Data

Student data will vary.

Data Table

Part A. Soil Texture			
Soil Particle Layer	**Sand (1 minute)**	**Sand + Silt (30 minutes)**	**Sand + Silt + Clay (24 hours)**
Height	3 mm	21 mm	22 mm
Color and appearance of water solution	Tan solution, slightly cloudy		

Part B. Dye Filtration			
Dye	**Filter Material**	**Color of Filtrate**	**Volume of Filtrate**
Methylene Blue	Soil	Colorless	7 mL
	Sand	Blue	18 mL
Eosin Y	Soil	Red	7 mL
	Sand	Red	16 mL

Part C. Chemical Properties			
Test	**pH**	**Nitrate**	**Phosphate**
Level or concentration	6.2 (using pH paper)	20 ppm	4 ppm

Answers to Post-Lab Questions *(Student answers will vary.)*

1. *(a)* Calculate the *percentages* of sand, silt, and clay in the soil sample: Divide the height of each respective soil layer by the combined height of all three layers, and multiply by 100.

    Combined height of soil layers = 22 mm

    Sand = (3/22) × 100% = 14%

    Silt = (18/22) × 100% = 82%

    Clay = (1/22) × 100% = 5%

    (b) Identify the soil texture class using the *soil texture triangle* (Figure 1).

    *Soil with 14% sand, 82% silt, and 5% clay is classified as **silt**.*

Teacher Notes

2. Compare and contrast the results of the dye filtration experiment:

(a) Which dye was retained (adsorbed) by the soil sample? How do you know?

The original methylene blue dye solution was dark blue. The filtrate obtained when this dye solution was passed through the soil "filter" was colorless—the dye was completely decolorized. This indicates that methylene blue was retained or adsorbed by the soil sample. **Note:** *This contrasts with the behavior of eosin Y. The soil filtrate was the same dark red color as the original dye solution.*

(b) Explain why one dye was retained by the soil while the other dye moved through the soil.

Soils readily bind or adsorb cations, not anions. Methylene blue is a cationic dye, eosin is an anionic dye. Only the cationic dye was removed or retained by the soil sample.

(c) What was the purpose of including sand in the design of this experiment?

Sand was included in this experiment as a control. Because of its large grain size, low surface area, and lack of charge (binding sites), sand does not bind either cations or anions.

3. Use the chemical test results from Part C to describe the soil quality:

(a) Is the soil acidic or basic?

The pH of the soil was 6.2, or slightly acidic. This is within the optimum range for soil quality (pH 6–7). Most plants grow well in this pH range.

(b) Are the levels of nitrates and phosphates suitable for plant growth? Explain.

Both the nitrate and phosphate levels, 20 ppm and 4 ppm, respectively, were adequate for plant growth. The phosphate concentration is a little high.

(c) Would you recommend that a fertilizer be applied to the soil before the next growing season? Why or why not?

Because there appears to be a surplus of phosphate already in the soil, only a light application of a **nitrogen-only fertilizer** *appears to be needed.*

4. Which type of soil particle has the largest *surface area* (surface-to-volume ratio)? How does this characteristic influence the physical and chemical properties of soil? Explain.

The amount of surface area is inversely related to particle size—smaller particles have a larger surface-to-volume ratio than larger particles. Clay particles therefore have the largest surface area compared to sand or silt. Surface area affects both the physical and chemical properties of soil. Clay soils are easily waterlogged, for example, because each tiny clay particle has a tendency to become coated with water. This increases the amount of water that a clay soil will hold. In addition, water does not drain well from clay because the pore sizes are very small. The ability of soil to bind and store nutrients is also related to the size and charge of clay particles. Adsorption occurs on the surface of particles, so the amount of material that can be bound to the soil increases as the surface area increases.

5. Explain why the pH of soil is an important aspect of soil fertility.

   The pH of soil is very important to soil fertility because the "soil solution" must dissolve and carry the nutrients plants need to grow. pH affects both the solubility of minerals and their availability to plants. In general, if the soil is too acidic (pH < 5.5), plants cannot utilize the nitrogen, phosphorus or potassium they need. The pH of soil also affects the viability of bacteria and other microorganisms in the soil. By helping to break down decaying plant and animal matter, microorganisms enrich the organic content of the soil.

6. Most state departments of agriculture recommend that farmers test their soil every year before applying fertilizers. What are the economic benefits of soil testing for the farmer? What are the general environmental benefits of soil testing?

   Testing the soil for macronutrients before applying fertilizers ensures that only the nutrients that are actually needed will be added to the soil. This cuts down on the amount of fertilizers and saves money. It also has a huge environmental benefit because high levels of nitrate and phosphate ions in water are a major factor in water pollution.

7. Describe the primary functions of nitrogen and phosphorus for plant growth. What are some natural sources of nitrates and phosphates in the soil?

   Nitrogen is an essential element for protein synthesis and is also needed for photosynthesis. There is thus a direct link between nitrogen levels in soil and overall plant nutrition and growth. Nitrogen is responsible for producing leaf growth and green leaves. Phosphorus is a major element in DNA and RNA, as well as cell membranes. It is important for seed development and for healthy roots. Nitrates originate in soils from decaying vegetation and animal wastes, and phosphates occur naturally in many soil minerals.

8. How do excess nitrates and phosphates from the soil end up in groundwater or surface water, respectively? Why is this a problem?

   Nitrate anions do not bind to soil—they get carried downward through the soil with water, finally ending up in groundwater. Groundwater is a major source of drinking water in many locations, and high nitrate levels in water make the water unfit to drink. Excess phosphate ions added to soil precipitate in the form of insoluble calcium phosphate, which binds to soil particles and gets washed away into surface water due to erosion or irrigation runoff. High levels of phosphate "fertilize" surface water and lead to unchecked algae growth and cultural eutrophication.

Supplementary Information

Determining the Percent Organic Matter in Soil

The amount of organic matter in soil is determined by combustion analysis. A sample of air-dried soil is dried at about 110 °C for 2 hours to remove all water, including waters of hydration in crystalline minerals such as gypsum. The soil is then heated to red-hot in a crucible using a Bunsen burner until a constant mass is obtained (typically 20–30 minutes). The amount of organic matter is calculated on a percentage basis using the difference in mass before and after heating.

Procedure

1. Measure and record the mass of an aluminum weighing dish or a glass Petri dish.

2. Add about 10 g of air-dried soil to the weighing dish and record the precise combined mass of the dish and the soil.

3. Place the weighing dish in an oven at 110 °C and allow the soil to dry for 2 hours.

4. Remove the weighing dish from the oven and place it in a desiccator to cool.

5. Measure and record the combined mass of the dry soil and the weighing dish.

6. Measure and record the mass of an empty 30-mL crucible and lid.

7. Add the dry soil to the crucible. Cover the crucible with the lid and measure the combined mass of the crucible, soil, and lid.

8. Set up a Bunsen burner on a ring stand beneath a ring clamp holding a clay, pipe-stem triangle. Do NOT light the Bunsen burner at this time.

9. Place the covered crucible at an angle on the clay triangle. Adjust the height of the ring clamp so that the bottom of the crucible is about 2 cm above the burner.

10. Light the Bunsen burner and brush the bottom of the crucible with the flame for 2–3 minutes to slowly heat the crucible and its contents.

11. Place the burner on the ring stand and heat the crucible in the hottest part of the flame for 15 minutes.

12. Turn off the gas source and remove the burner. Allow the crucible to cool for a few minutes, then place it in a desiccator to cool to room temperature.

13. Measure and record the mass of the crucible, lid, and its contents.

14. Repeat steps 9 and 10 and re-heat the crucible and its contents for *5 minutes*. Allow to cool and measure and record the mass.

15. Repeat as necessary until constant mass is achieved—the mass should not change by more than 0.02 g between readings.

Teacher's Notes

Sample Data

Percent Organic Matter in Soil	Trial 1	Trial 2
Mass of aluminum weighing dish	1.14 g	1.15 g
Mass of dish and air-dried soil (before heating)	11.26 g	21.56 g
Mass of dish and soil (after heating at 110 °C for 2 hr)	11.06 g	21.11 g
Percent water loss	2.0%	2.2%
Mass of crucible and lid	31.75 g	35.28 g
Mass of crucible, lid, and soil (before heating)	41.67 g	45.15 g
Mass of crucible, lid, and soil (after heating red-hot—15 min)	40.70 g	44.02 g
Mass of crucible, lid, and soil (after heating another 5 min)	40.61 g	44.00 g
Percent organic matter	10.7%	11.7%

Flinn ChemTopic Labs — Chemistry in the Environment 16

pH and the Alkalinity of Water
Buffer Capacity and Water Quality

Introduction

The pH of water is an important indicator of water quality—most aquatic organisms require a fairly narrow pH range in order to survive and reproduce. Just as living cells contain natural buffer systems to control pH, many lakes, rivers, and streams are also naturally buffered due to the presence of dissolved minerals from soil and rocks. The buffering capacity of water is called its alkalinity. What is alkalinity and how is it measured?

Concepts

- Acids, bases, and pH
- Buffers and buffer capacity
- Alkalinity
- Acid rain and water pollution

Background

Pure water contains extremely small but equal amounts of hydrogen ions (H^+) and hydroxide ions (OH^-). Acids and bases are substances that alter the concentrations of H^+ and OH^- ions in water. When water contains more H^+ ions than OH^- ions, it is considered acidic, and when it contains more OH^- ions than H^+ ions, it is considered basic. The relative acidity or basicity of water can be compared by measuring the pH. The pH scale ranges from 0 (very acidic) to 14 (highly basic). pH 7 is neutral, pH <7 is acidic, and pH >7 is basic. Recall that a difference of one pH unit corresponds to a tenfold difference in the concentration of H^+ ions.

The pH of most natural bodies of water in the United States is between 6.5 and 8.5. In general, water becomes unsuitable for aquatic life when the pH is less than 5 or greater than 9. Healthy freshwater lakes and streams are usually slightly basic, with a pH of 8. In many areas of the country, the surface waters contain dissolved carbonate and bicarbonate ions from limestone sediments and weathered bedrock. (Limestone is calcium carbonate.) These dissolved ions make the water slightly basic and also provide a natural buffer, neutralizing acid rain or snow and helping to regulate the pH level in the water. In some regions of the country, particularly in the northeastern United States and the Rocky Mountain states, the bedrock is granite and the surface waters are not buffered. Chronic acidity has a negative effect on water quality, aquatic life, and ecological diversity. The changes may be gradual at first, as snails, crayfish, insect larvae, and young fish are affected. The initial changes are followed by a domino effect that disturbs the entire ecosystem. (1) There is a progressive loss of the most sensitive species of fish, such as trout and bass; (2) algae, mosses, and fungal mats pollute the water; and (3) waterfowl suffer as the quality of their habitat declines.

A buffer is a solution that resists changes in pH when acids or bases are added to it. *Alkalinity* is defined as the buffering capacity of water—its ability to neutralize hydrogen ions and maintain a stable pH. Although other ions, including phosphates and borates, may also contribute, alkalinity in freshwater is due primarily to bicarbonate (HCO_3^-) and carbonate (CO_3^{2-}) ions.

The alkalinity of water is related to water hardness (both are expressed in terms of ppm $CaCO_3$), but they are not identical. Divide the class in half and have one half of the students do the alkalinity titration in this experiment while the other half determines water hardness. (See "How Hard Is Your Water?" beginning on page 29.) Compare the results obtained by the two groups and discuss why alkalinity is not equivalent to water hardness. Water hardness may be due to other minerals, such as $CaCl_2$, $CaSO_4$, $FeCl_3$, etc.

The alkalinity of water is determined by titration with dilute acid, measuring the amount of acid that must be added to lower the pH to about 4. The results are analyzed by assuming that (1) all of the H⁺ ions are neutralized by CO_3^{2-} ions from dissolved calcium carbonate, and (2) one mole of CO_3^{2-} ions reacts with two moles of H⁺ ions. See Equations 1 and 2.

$$CaCO_3(s) \rightarrow Ca^{2+}(aq) + CO_3^{2-}(aq) \qquad \textit{Equation 1}$$

$$CO_3^{2-}(aq) + 2H^+(aq) \rightarrow H_2CO_3 \rightarrow CO_2(g) + H_2O(l) \qquad \textit{Equation 2}$$

Alkalinity is calculated in terms of milligrams of calcium carbonate per liter (mg/L) of water, or parts per million (ppm) of calcium carbonate. (A concentration of 1 mg $CaCO_3$/L is equal to 1 ppm.) Typical alkalinity levels for freshwater are 50–200 ppm. Alkalinity levels of 100–200 ppm are generally sufficient to protect the pH in a lake or stream from acid rain, mining and industrial discharges or waste, and decaying organic matter. High alkalinity is usually present in water that flows over limestone and sedimentary rocks or carbonate-rich soils. Although there are no standards for alkalinity, very high alkalinity is also associated with excessive water hardness, which is undesirable in drinking water. Low alkalinity levels are common in mountain streams and other regions where igneous rocks predominate. Alkalinity values less than 30 ppm indicate that water is poorly buffered and prone to acidification.

Although alkalinity is calculated in terms of the amount of calcium carbonate, bicarbonate ions are the principal species present when calcium carbonate dissolves in water containing carbon dioxide (Equation 3). The "natural" pH of this solution is about 8—the average pH of most freshwater lakes and streams.

$$CaCO_3(s) + H_2O(l) + CO_2(g) \rightarrow Ca^{2+}(aq) + 2HCO_3^-(aq) \qquad \textit{Equation 3}$$

The ability of a buffer to maintain a stable pH can be explained in terms of the chemical composition. All buffers contain a weak acid and its conjugate base, or a weak base and its conjugate acid. These components will neutralize either acid or base that may be added. Bicarbonate ions are both a weak acid and a weak base—and an excellent buffer. As long as carbon dioxide, carbonate ions, and bicarbonate ions are present, the pH will stay relatively constant (Figure 1). The buffering capacity of a lake or stream may be overwhelmed if acid is continually added and the alkalinity is not replenished from soil or rocks.

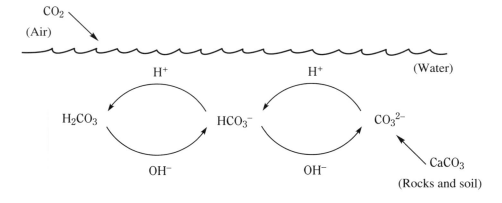

Figure 1. Model of a Bicarbonate Buffer.

Teacher Notes

Experiment Overview

The purpose of this experiment is to determine the alkalinity of water. Different water samples may be tested: Tap water, pond water, river water, etc. The alkalinity will be analyzed by titrating with dilute hydrochloric acid, either 0.1 M or 0.02 M HCl, depending on the alkalinity levels, to a methyl orange endpoint. The indicator methyl orange is red when the pH is less than 3.0 and yellow when the pH is greater than 4.4.

Pre-Lab Questions

The alkalinity of pond water was analyzed by titration with dilute hydrochloric acid to a methyl orange endpoint. The following results were obtained:

Volume of pond water	100.0 mL
Molarity of HCl solution	0.0975 M
Volume of HCl added	5.90 mL

1. How many *moles* of hydrochloric acid were added to the sample?

2. Calculate the *mass* (in milligrams) of calcium carbonate that was neutralized by this number of moles of hydrochloric acid.

3. Divide the mass of calcium carbonate by the volume of pond water to determine the alkalinity. *Recall:* Alkalinity is usually expressed in ppm, where 1 ppm = 1 mg $CaCO_3$/L.

Materials

Hydrochloric acid, HCl, 0.100 M and 0.020 M (standard solutions), 50 mL each

Methyl orange indicator, 0.1% solution, 2 mL

Water samples (pond water, river water, tap water, rain or melted snow, etc.), 300 mL

pH meter or pH test paper, narrow range, 6.0–8.0 and 8.0–9.5

Beakers, 100- and 400-mL	Graduated cylinder, 100-mL
Beral-type pipet	Erlenmeyer flasks, 250-mL, 2
Buret, 25- or 50-mL	Support (ring) stand
Buret clamp	Wash bottle and distilled water

Safety Precautions

Dilute hydrochloric acid solution may be irritating to the skin and eyes. Wear chemical splash goggles, chemical-resistant gloves, and a chemical-resistant apron. Avoid contact of all chemicals with skin and eyes and wash hands thoroughly with soap and water before leaving the lab.

Procedure

1. Obtain about 300 mL of the water to be analyzed in a 400-mL beaker. Measure the initial pH of the water using a pH meter or narrow-range pH paper. Record the source of the water and the pH in the data table.

2. Obtain about 50 mL of 0.1 M standard hydrochloric acid solution in a small beaker, and record the precise molarity of the solution in the data table.

3. Pour about 100 mL of distilled water into a clean Erlenmeyer flask, and add 5 drops of methyl orange indicator solution. Observe the initial color of the solution, and then add two drops of 0.1 M HCl to the water. Record the final color of the solution. This solution will be used as a *color standard* to determine the endpoint (step 16).

Follow steps 4–6 to determine which standard HCl solution should be used in the titration:

4. Obtain 50 mL of the water sample to be analyzed to a 100-mL beaker. Add 3–5 drops of methyl orange indicator solution and observe the color.

5. Add 2 mL of the 0.100 M standard HCl solution to the water sample. Swirl the solution and observe the color.

6. If the color changed to the "endpoint color" observed in step 3, then use the 0.020 M standard HCl solution in the titration (steps 7–16). If the indicator color did not change, use 0.100 M standard HCl solution in the titration.

7. Rinse a 25-mL buret with distilled water and then with two 5-mL portions of the appropriate standard HCl solution.

8. Clamp the buret to a ring stand and place a small "waste" beaker under the buret.

9. Fill the buret to above the zero mark with the standard HCl solution. Open the stopcock to allow any air bubbles to escape from the tip. Close the stopcock when the liquid level in the buret is between the 0- and 5-mL mark.

10. Measure and record the *initial volume* of the HCl solution in the buret. *Note:* Volumes are read from the top down in a buret. Always read from the bottom of the meniscus, and remember to include the proper number of significant figures.

11. Rinse the Erlenmeyer flask and the graduated cylinder with distilled water. Using the graduated cylinder, transfer 100.0 mL of the water sample to be analyzed to the Erlenmeyer flask.

12. Add 3–5 drops of methyl orange indicator to the water sample.

13. Position the Erlenmeyer flask under the buret so that the tip of the buret is inside the mouth of the flask. Place a sheet of white paper under the flask.

14. Open the stopcock and add about 1 mL of HCl to the water sample. Observe the color changes.

15. Continue the titration: Add HCl slowly, about 0.2 mL at a time, while swirling the flask. Use a wash bottle to rinse the sides of the flask only if necessary.

16. When the indicator color changes from yellow to peach, slow down the titration and add HCl drop-by-drop until the color of the water in the flask matches the "endpoint color" (step 3). Close the stopcock and record the *final volume* of the HCl in the buret.

17. Pour the solution out of the flask and rinse the flask with distilled water. Repeat the titration (steps 10–16) with a fresh sample of water and record all data in the data table.

Name: _____

Class/Lab Period: _____

pH and the Alkalinity of Water

Data Table

Analysis of Water		
Concentration of HCl Solution		
Water Source	**Initial pH**	**Endpoint Color**
Titration Data	**Trial 1**	**Trial 2**
Initial Volume of HCl		
Final Volume of HCl		
Volume of HCl Added		

Post-Lab Questions *(Use a separate sheet of paper to answer the following questions.)*

1. For each trial, calculate (a) the number of moles of HCl required to neutralize the water, and (b) the mass of calcium carbonate corresponding to this amount of hydrochloric acid.

2. Divide the mass of calcium carbonate by the volume of water to determine the alkalinity of the water for each trial.

3. (a) What is the average alkalinity of the water sample? (b) Describe the buffering capacity of the water—low, medium, high, etc. Explain.

4. The terms basicity and alkalinity are frequently misunderstood. What is the difference between the two terms? Is it possible for water to be basic yet have very low alkalinity?

5. A 0.1 M sodium bicarbonate solution has a pH of about 8.4. What is the volume of 0.1 M HCl solution that could be neutralized by one liter of 0.1 M $NaHCO_3$?

6. In addition to providing buffering capacity (alkalinity), high concentrations of carbonate ions also prevent the release of hazardous heavy metals into the water. Write balanced chemical equations for the precipitation reactions of cadmium, lead, and mercury ions with carbonate ions.

7. How do automobile exhaust and smokestack emissions contribute to acid rain?

Teacher's Notes
pH and the Alkalinity of Water

Master Materials List *(for a class of 30 students working in pairs)*

Hydrochloric acid, HCl, 0.100 M and 0.020 M (standard solutions), 750 mL each*

Methyl orange indicator, 0.1% solution, 50 mL

Water samples (pond or river water, tap water, rain or melted snow), 300 mL each

pH meter or pH test paper, narrow range, 6.0–8.0 and 8.0–9.5

Beakers, 100- and 400-mL, 15 each	Graduated cylinders, 100-mL, 15
Beral-type pipets, 15	Erlenmeyer flasks, 250-mL, 30
Burets, 25- or 50-mL, 15	Support (ring) stands, 15
Buret clamps, 15	Wash bottles and distilled water, 15

See the Teaching Tips *section.*

Preparation of Solutions *(for a class of 30 students working in pairs)*

Hydrochloric Acid, 0.1 M: Add about 500 mL of distilled or deionized water to a flask. Carefully add 8.3 mL of concentrated hydrochloric acid. Stir to mix, then dilute to 1 L with distilled water. Determine the precise molarity of the solution by titrating it with standard sodium hydroxide solution. *Note:* Sodium hydroxide is standardized with potassium hydrogen phthalate (KHP). See the *Lab Hints* and the *Supplementary Information* sections.

Hydrochloric Acid, 0.02 M: Dilute the standardized 0.1 M hydrochloric acid solution by a factor of five. Measure 200.0 mL of 0.1 M HCl solution using a pipet or graduated cylinder and dilute to 1 L in a volumetric flask. Determine the precise molarity.

Methyl Orange, 0.1%: Dissolve 0.1 g of methyl orange indicator (solid) in 100 mL of distilled or deionized water.

Safety Precautions

Dilute hydrochloric acid solution may be irritating to the skin and eyes. Wear chemical splash goggles, chemical-resistant gloves, and a chemical-resistant apron. Please review current Material Safety Data Sheets for additional safety, handling, and disposal information. Remind students to wash hands thoroughly with soap and water before leaving the lab.

Disposal

Please consult your current *Flinn Scientific Catalog/Reference Manual* for general guidelines and specific procedures governing the disposal of laboratory waste. The dilute HCl solution should be neutralized prior to rinsing down the drain. See Flinn Suggested Disposal Method #24b.

Teacher Notes

Lab Hints

- The lab work for this experiment can reasonably be completed in one 50-minute class period. Students should be familiar with setting up a buret and with general titration techniques. Review the *Pre-Lab Questions* prior to lab to familiarize students with the calculations needed to analyze the results.

- To make the lab more interesting and also to promote student "investment" in the results, encourage students to bring in water samples for study. Comparing water from different sources will help students understand both the origin and the causes of alkalinity. In many areas of the country, tap or drinking water that is obtained from groundwater is likely to be very hard and also to have high alkalinity. Creeks or streams that are sampled after a heavy rainfall (or a spring thaw) will have low alkalinity values.

- The equivalence point for alkalinity titrations is traditionally (and arbitrarily) defined at pH 4.5. This is based on the assumption that carbonate is the main buffering component and that the major ions present are HCO_3^-, CO_3^{2-}, and OH^-. Hydroxide ions are present in *minor* amounts when the pH is less than 10. The "hydroxide alkalinity" can be determined by preliminary titration to a phenolphthalein endpoint, if desired. The pK_{a1} value for carbonic acid (H_2CO_3) is 6.4. When the pH $= pK_a - 2$, all of the carbonate ions will have reacted, and no further reaction with H^+ ions is possible—the buffering capacity is exhausted. If other ions such as phosphates, silicates, borates, and organic acids, etc., are present, the actual or true equivalence point will be closer to pH 5.

- Using a color standard to identify the endpoint improves accuracy in the titrations. The yellow to pink transition (from basic to acidic) goes through various shades of peach and is therefore hard to discern precisely.

- Bromcresol green may also be used to detect the endpoint in alkalinity titrations. The color change for bromcresol green occurs between 3.8 and 5.4 (yellow when the pH <3.8, blue when the pH >5.4, and green in between).

- For a supplementary exercise, students can obtain rough titration curve data (pH versus volume of HCl added) by measuring the pH as acid is added in 0.5-mL increments. Comparing the titration curves of buffered and unbuffered water samples provides persuasive visual evidence for the properties of a buffer.

Teaching Tips

- The precise concentration of HCl can be determined by titrating it against a standard sodium hydroxide solution. The *Supplementary Information* section has a written procedure for standardizing NaOH using potassium hydrogen phthalate (KHP).

- The United States Geological Society collects data on the deposition of acid rain and snow at 250 sites across the country. It also monitors the pH of lakes and streams and assesses the effects of acid rain on water quality, aquatic life, and the surrounding land areas. The USGS Web site provides a wealth of resources: http://bqs.usgs.gov/acidrain/

- The overall equation for the formation of bicarbonate ions when calcium carbonate dissolves in water (see Equation 3 in the *Background* section) is the sum of the equations for the following reversible reactions (Reactions 3a–3e). The concentration of bicarbonate ions can be calculated since the equilibrium constants for each reaction are known.

$$CO_2(aq) + H_2O(l) \rightleftharpoons H_2CO_3(aq) \qquad\qquad \textit{Reaction 3a}$$

$$H_2CO_3(aq) \rightleftharpoons HCO_3^-(aq) + H^+(aq) \qquad\qquad \textit{Reaction 3b}$$

$$H^+(aq) + OH^-(aq) \rightleftharpoons H_2O(l) \qquad\qquad \textit{Reaction 3c}$$

$$CaCO_3(s) \rightleftharpoons Ca^{2+}(aq) + CO_3^{2-}(aq) \qquad\qquad \textit{Reaction 3d}$$

$$CO_3^{2-}(aq) + H_2O(l) \rightleftharpoons HCO_3^-(aq) + OH^-(aq) \qquad\qquad \textit{Reaction 3e}$$

$$CaCO_3(s) + H_2O(l) + CO_2(g) \rightleftharpoons Ca^{2+}(aq) + 2HCO_3^-(aq) \qquad \textit{Equation 3}$$

Answers to Pre-Lab Questions *(Student answers will vary.)*

The alkalinity of pond water was analyzed by titration with dilute hydrochloric acid to a methyl orange endpoint. The following results were obtained:

Volume of pond water	100.0 mL
Molarity of HCl solution	0.0975 M
Volume of HCl added	5.90 mL

1. How many *moles* of hydrochloric acid were added to the sample?

   Multiply the molarity (moles per liter) of the HCl solution by the volume (in liters) of HCl added to the sample.

   $0.0975\ M \times 0.00590\ L = 5.75 \times 10^{-4}\ moles\ HCl$

2. Calculate the *mass* (in milligrams) of calcium carbonate that was neutralized by this number of moles of hydrochloric acid.

   The mole ratio for the neutralization reaction is 2 moles of HCl per mole of $CaCO_3$.

   $(5.75 \times 10^{-4}\ moles\ HCl) \times \dfrac{1\ mole\ CaCO_3}{2\ moles\ HCl} = 2.88 \times 10^{-4}\ moles\ CaCO_3$

   $(2.88 \times 10^{-4}\ moles\ CaCO_3) \times \dfrac{100.1\ g}{1\ mole} \times \dfrac{1000\ mg}{1\ g} = 28.8\ mg$

3. Divide the mass of calcium carbonate by the volume of pond water to determine the alkalinity. *Recall:* Alkalinity is usually expressed in ppm, where 1 ppm = 1 mg $CaCO_3$/L.

   The volume of pond water was 100 mL (0.10 L).

   Alkalinity = 28.8 mg/0.1 L = 288 ppm

Sample Data

Student data will vary.

Data Table

Analysis of Water		
Concentration of HCl Solution	0.0991 M	
Water Source	**Initial pH**	**Endpoint Color**
Tap water	7.4	Salmon pink (dark pink)
Titration Data	**Trial 1**	**Trial 2**
Initial Volume of HCl	0.02 mL	5.00 mL
Final Volume of HCl	4.95 mL	10.10 mL
Volume of HCl Added	4.93 mL	5.10 mL

Answers to Post-Lab Questions *(Student answers will vary.)*

1. For each trial, calculate (a) the number of moles of HCl required to neutralize the water, and (b) the mass of calcium carbonate corresponding to this amount of hydrochloric acid.

    (a) *Trial 1 $(0.0991M)(0.00493 L) = 4.89 \times 10^{-4}$ moles HCl*

    Trial 2 5.05×10^{-4} moles HCl

    (b) *Trial 1 $(4.89 \times 10^{-4}$ moles HCl$) \dfrac{(1\ mole\ CaCO_3)}{(2\ moles\ HCl)} = 2.45 \times 10^{-4}$ moles $CaCO_3$*

    $$2.45 \times 10^{-4}\ moles\ CaCO_3 \times \frac{100.1\ g}{1\ mole} \times \frac{1000\ mg}{1\ g} = 24.5\ mg$$

    Trial 2   25.3 mg

2. Divide the mass of calcium carbonate by the volume of water to determine the alkalinity of the water for each trial.

    Alkalinity: 24.5 mg/0.100 L = 245 ppm (Trial 1)
    25.3 mg/0.100 L = 253 ppm (Trial 2)

3. (a) What is the average alkalinity of the water sample? (b) Describe the buffering capacity of the water—low, medium, high, etc. Explain.

    (a) *The average alkalinity is 250 ppm.*

    (b) *This is in the high range—the buffering capacity is excellent.*

4. The terms basicity and alkalinity are frequently misunderstood. What is the difference between the two terms? Is it possible for water to be basic yet have very low alkalinity?

   Basicity refers to the relative concentration of OH⁻ and H⁺ ions: There is an excess of OH⁻ ions compared to pure water. Alkalinity is the ability of water to neutralize H⁺ ions that might be added to the water (the buffering capacity). Although OH⁻ ions will neutralize H⁺ ions, most of the buffering capacity is due to other ions in the water, principally HCO_3^- and CO_3^{2-} ions. The concentration of these ions may be several orders of magnitude higher than the concentration of OH⁻ ions. If hydroxide ions are the principal ions present in water, the water will be basic but have low alkalinity.

   Note to teachers: *The following example may help students understand the difference between these two terms. A 0.001 M sodium hydroxide solution would be very basic (pH 11). One liter of this solution, however, would neutralize only 10 mL of 0.1 M HCl. See also the answer to Question #5 below.*

5. A 0.1 M sodium bicarbonate solution has a pH of about 8.4. What is the volume of 0.1 M HCl solution that could be neutralized by one liter of 0.1 M $NaHCO_3$?

   The neutralization mole ratio for the reaction of $NaHCO_3$ with HCl is 1:1.

   One liter of 0.1 M $NaHCO_3$ will neutralize 1 L (an equivalent volume) of 0.1 M HCl.

6. In addition to providing buffering capacity (alkalinity), high concentrations of carbonate ions also prevent the release of hazardous heavy metals into the water. Write balanced chemical equations for the precipitation reactions of cadmium, lead, and mercury ions with carbonate ions.

   All of these heavy metal cations are divalent (+2 charge). Example:

   $Pb^{2+}(aq) + CO_3^{2-}(aq) \rightarrow PbCO_3(s)$

7. How do automobile exhaust and smokestack emissions contribute to acid rain?

   Automobile exhaust and industrial emissions release combustion products such as nitrogen oxides (NO_x) and sulfur dioxide (SO_2) into the atmosphere. These gases are converted to nitrogen dioxide and sulfur trioxide, which then combine with water in the air to form nitric acid and sulfuric acid. The latter strong acids are the principal components of acid rain.

Supplementary Information

Standardization Procedure for Sodium Hydroxide Solution

1. Obtain a sample of potassium hydrogen phthalate (KHP) that has been previously dried in an oven and stored in a desiccator.

2. On an analytical balance, accurately weigh 0.4 to 0.6 grams of KHP in a previously tared weighing dish. Record the precise mass of KHP.

3. Transfer the KHP into an Erlenmeyer flask—pour the solid through a funnel into the flask. Use water from a wash bottle to rinse all of the remaining solid from the weighing dish or the funnel into the flask as well.

4. Add about 40 mL of distilled or deionized water to the Erlenmeyer flask and swirl until all the KHP is dissolved.

5. Add three drops of phenolphthalein solution to the KHP solution in the flask.

6. Fill a buret with the sodium hydroxide solution to be standardized and titrate the KHP solution until the pink color persists for 15 seconds.

7. Repeat the titration two more times. Rinse the Erlenmeyer flask thoroughly between trials with distilled or deionized water.

Sample Data

	Trial 1	Trial 2	Trial 3
Mass KHP, g	0.422 g	0.390 g	0.475 g
Final Volume, mL	23.20 mL	26.50 mL	24.00 mL
Initial Volume, mL	3.30 mL	7.80 mL	2.10 mL
Volume of NaOH added, mL	19.90 mL	18.70 mL	22.90 mL

Molarity NaOH (Average) __0.103__ M

Teacher Notes

How Hard Is Your Water?
Microscale Titration

Introduction

As water flows through rocks and soil, it picks up minerals from the Earth's surface. Although many minerals are essential for life and health and thus desirable, high levels of calcium, magnesium, and iron in "hard water" may cause nuisance problems at home as well as in industry. What is water hardness and how is it analyzed?

Concepts

- Water hardness
- EDTA titration
- Chelates and complex ions
- Water softening

Background

Tap water contains a large number of dissolved ions: calcium (Ca^{2+}), magnesium (Mg^{2+}), iron (Fe^{3+}), and sodium (Na^+) cations, along with chloride (Cl^-), sulfate (SO_4^{2-}), bicarbonate (HCO_3^-), and nitrate (NO_3^-) anions. When tap water is boiled for a long period of time, it begins to leave a film or residue on the walls of the container. White, scaly deposits, called water scale, are often observed in pots or pans at home, on beakers and flasks in the laboratory, and inside pipes and tanks in appliances. Water scale consists primarily of calcium and magnesium carbonate, along with the corresponding sulfate salts. When the quantity of these salts is high, the water is described as being hard. *Water hardness* is defined as the total concentration of calcium and magnesium ions in water.

Ordinary soaps form a precipitate in hard water—they do not give a good lather or clean efficiently, and they leave an insoluble residue (soap scum) on skin, clothing, bathtubs, and sinks. Synthetic detergents perform the same functions as soap, but because they are soluble in hard water, they do not leave a residue. This is one reason why synthetic detergents are used instead of soap to clean clothing. Hard water also builds up scale deposits inside water heaters and other appliances, as well as in industrial pipes or boilers, reducing their heating capacity and efficiency.

The amount of calcium and magnesium ions in water is determined by titration with a metal complexing agent called ethylenediaminetetraacetic acid, mercifully abbreviated EDTA. EDTA reacts with metal ions, including calcium and magnesium, to form stable complex ions (Equation 1).

$$Ca^{2+}(aq) + EDTA(aq) \rightarrow Ca^{2+}\text{–}EDTA \qquad \textit{Equation 1}$$
$$\textit{Complex ion}$$

In basic solution (pH >10), EDTA has a –4 charge due to four negatively charged oxygen atoms. As shown in Figures 1 and 2, the oxygen and nitrogen atoms in EDTA wrap around a metal ion and surround it. The resulting complex ion is called a *chelate,* from the Greek word "chelos," meaning claw. The analogy is that EDTA is like a claw, trapping the metal ion and keeping it tightly in its grip. Chelation therapy involves the clinical use of EDTA and other metal complexing agents as antidotes for heavy metal poisoning. The EDTA molecules

Soaps and detergents are considered surface-active agents or surfactants. They reduce the surface tension of water, improve the wettability of skin and fabrics, and help to emulcify grease and dirt. Soaps are water-soluble sodium salts of fatty acids abtained by the hydrolysis of naturally occuring fats and oils. Detergents are synthetic linear alkyl sulfonates such as $CH_{13}(CH_2)_9SO_3^-Na^+$.

bind to lead ions in the stomach, for example, and cause the metal ions to pass harmlessly out of the body.

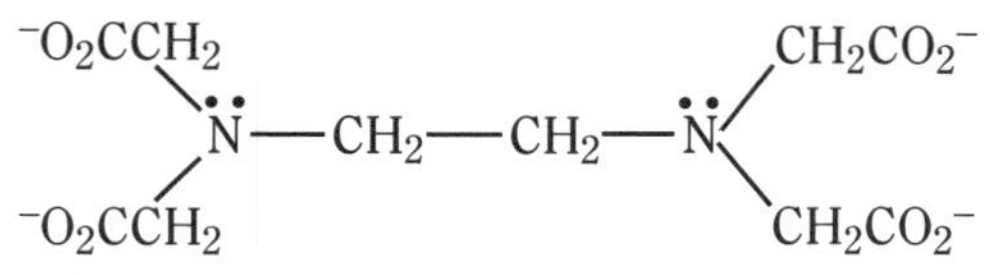

Figure 1. Structure of EDTA. 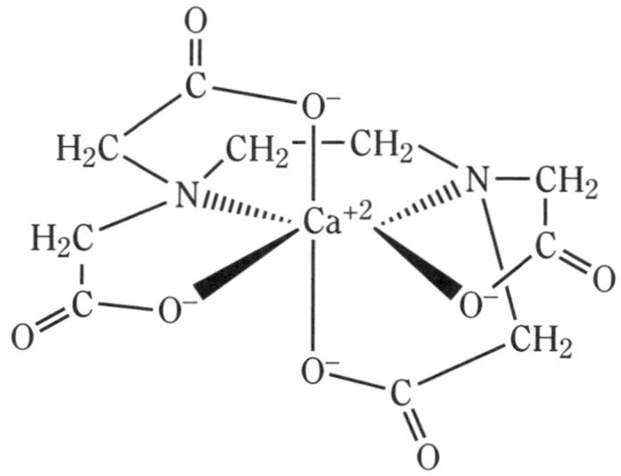   **Figure 2.** EDTA–Ca^{2+} Complex Ion (Chelate).

In the titration of hard water with EDTA, the point at which all of the Ca^{2+} and Mg^{2+} ions have reacted with EDTA is called the endpoint. Because Ca^{2+} and Mg^{2+} ions, and the resulting complex ions, are all colorless, a *metal-ion indicator* (Ind) such as calmagite must be added to detect the endpoint. (A metal-ion indicator is a compound that changes color when bound to a metal ion.) In the case of calmagite, the solution starts out pink, the color of the Ca^{2+}–Ind complex ion. At the endpoint, the last drop of EDTA added dislodges the indicator from the Ca^{2+}–Ind complex (Equation 2) and the solution turns blue, which is the color of unbound Ind. The indicator color change signals the end of the titration. The titration is carried out in a pH 10 buffer, which keeps the solution basic and ensures that EDTA will exist in its most active form.

$$Ca^{2+}\text{–Ind} + EDTA \rightarrow Ca^{2+}\text{–EDTA} + Ind \qquad \textit{Equation 2}$$
$$\textit{Pink} \qquad\qquad \textit{Colorless} \quad \textit{Blue}$$

Several different metal ions contribute to water hardness. Hardness levels are calculated by *assuming* that all of the metal ions that react with EDTA come from dissolved calcium carbonate. Water hardness is typically reported in terms of milligrams of calcium carbonate per liter of water (mg $CaCO_3$/L) or parts per million (ppm), where 1 ppm = 1 mg $CaCO_3$/L. The U.S. Geological Survey classifies water hardness levels as follows: soft water, <60 ppm; moderately hard, 60–120 ppm; hard water, 120–180 ppm; and very hard, >180 ppm.

Commercial water softeners for home and industrial use utilize ion-exchange resins to remove calcium and magnesium ions from hard water. The ion-exchange resin consists of polymer "beads" with negatively charged groups covalently bonded to the polymer structure. Each negative charge in the polymer structure is balanced by a sodium cation. When hard water is passed through the resin, calcium and magnesium ions bind to the negatively charged groups on the polymer and displace sodium ions. The calcium and magnesium ions in water are thus replaced by sodium cations, which do not contribute to water hardness.

Teacher Notes

Experiment Overview

The purpose of this experiment is to analyze water hardness by *microscale titration* with EDTA. The titrant (EDTA) will be added dropwise using a microtip pipet. (Microtip pipets have fine tips, making it easier to deliver drops that are always the same size or volume.) Water hardness levels for tap water, pool water, etc. will be determined using a *standard graph* obtained by plotting the number of drops of EDTA versus water hardness (ppm) for a set of standard solutions containing 60, 120, and 180 ppm $CaCO_3$.

Pre-Lab Questions

1. What is the charge on the EDTA anion in strongly basic solution (pH 10)? What is the overall charge on the *complex ion* when a Ca^{2+} or Mg^{2+} ion is bound to EDTA?

2. The metal-ion indicator in an EDTA titration must bind to metal ions less strongly than EDTA does. Explain what would happen if the reverse were true.

3. A standard solution was prepared by dissolving 200 mg of calcium chloride ($CaCl_2$) in one liter of water. Calculate the equivalent water hardness in terms of ppm $CaCO_3$.

Materials

Buffer solution, pH 10, 5 mL

Calmagite indicator solution, 0.05%, 3 mL

Distilled or deionized water

EDTA solution, 0.0075 M, 15 mL

Standard solutions, 60, 120, and 180 ppm $CaCO_3$, 10 mL each

Tap water, pond or river water, pool water, etc.

Beral-type pipets, thin-stem, 2

Microtip, Beral-type pipet

Reaction plate, 24-well

Syringe (w/o needle), 3-mL

Toothpicks, plastic (to stir), 5

Paper

Wash bottle

Safety Precautions

The pH 10 buffer solution is a body tissue irritant and is mildly toxic by ingestion. The solution may release harmful vapors—do not breathe the fumes. Wear chemical splash goggles, chemical-resistant gloves, and a chemical-resistant apron. Avoid contact of all chemicals with skin and eyes and wash hands with soap and water before leaving the lab.

Procedure

1. Rinse the 24-well reaction plate with distilled water and shake dry. Place the reaction plate on a piece of white paper.

2. Rinse a 3-mL syringe or 10-mL graduated cylinder with distilled water.

3. Using the syringe or graduated cylinder, measure and add 1.5 mL of distilled water to well A1 in the reaction plate. This is the blank solution.

4. Add 5 drops of pH 10 buffer to the water, followed by 2 drops of Calmagite indicator. Observe the initial color.

5. Using a microtip pipet, add one drop of 0.0075 M EDTA solution to well A1 and stir with a plastic toothpick—the water should turn blue. The color of this solution will be used for comparison to determine the endpoint in each titration (see step 9).

6. Rinse the syringe or graduated cylinder with tap water.

7. Measure and add 1.5 mL of tap water to each of three adjacent wells, A2, B2, and C2.

8. Add 5 drops of pH 10 buffer, followed by 2 drops of Calmagite, to each tap water sample (wells A2, B2, and C2). Stir with a clean toothpick.

9. Using a microtip pipet, slowly add EDTA one drop at a time to the tap water sample in well A2. Count the exact number of drops that must be added for the solution to turn blue (compare to the color standard in well A1). Record the number of drops of EDTA in the data table.

10. Repeat step 9 twice more using the tap water samples in wells B2 and C2. Count and record the exact number of drops of EDTA that must be added to reach the endpoint.

11. Rinse the syringe with the 60 ppm standard solution.

12. Measure and add 1.5 mL of the 60 ppm standard solution to each of three adjacent wells, A3, B3, and C3.

13. Add 5 drops of pH 10 buffer, followed by 2 drops of Calmagite, to each 60 ppm standard solution (wells A3, B3, and C3). Stir with a clean toothpick.

14. Using a microtip pipet, add EDTA slowly one drop at a time to the first standard solution (well A3). Count the exact number of drops of EDTA that must be added for the solution to turn blue (compare to the color standard in well A1). Record the number of drops in the data table.

15. Repeat step 14 twice more using the 60 ppm samples in wells B3 and C3. Count and record the exact number of drops of EDTA that must be added to reach the endpoint.

16. Repeat steps 11–15 twice more, using first the 120 ppm standard solution (wells A4, B4, and C4) and then the 180 ppm standard solution (wells A5, B5, and C5).

17. *(Optional)* Repeat the EDTA titration using other water samples (pond water, river water, aquarium water, pool water, well water, etc.).

18. Calculate and record the average number of drops of EDTA added for each standard solution and water sample.

The blue endpoint color in the distilled water standard (step 5) may fade over time. If this happens, have students repeat steps 3–5 to prepare a fresh color standard for comparison.

Teacher Notes

Name: _____

Class/Lab Period: _____

How Hard Is Your Water?

Data Table

Sample	Number of Drops of EDTA Added			
	Trial 1	Trial 2	Trial 3	Average
Tap Water				
Standard Solution (60 ppm $CaCO_3$)				
Standard Solution (120 ppm $CaCO_3$)				
Standard Solution (180 ppm $CaCO_3$)				
Other (Pool water)				

Post-Lab Questions *(Use a separate sheet of paper to answer the following questions.)*

1. Graph the titration results for the *standard solutions:* Plot the average number of drops of EDTA added on the *y*-axis versus water hardness in ppm $CaCO_3$ on the *x*-axis. Using a ruler or straightedge, draw a best-fit straight line through the origin and the data points.

2. (a) Why is the origin included in this line? (b) Explain in principle how this graph can be used to determine the water hardness in an "unknown" sample.

3. Using the graph, determine the water hardness in ppm $CaCO_3$ for tap water and any other water samples analyzed. Classify the hardness level: soft water, hard water, very hard, etc.

4. A sample of pool water was analyzed by EDTA titration using a buret:

   Volume of water tested   50.0 mL
   Concentration of EDTA   0.010 M
   Volume of EDTA added   15.4 mL

   Calculate (a) the number of moles of EDTA added at the endpoint; (b) the equivalent mass of calcium carbonate in the pool water that reacted with EDTA; and (c) the water hardness level in parts per million (1 ppm = 1 mg $CaCO_3$/L).

5. Many municipal water treatment plants use lime [$Ca(OH)_2$] and soda ash (Na_2CO_3) to chemically remove calcium and magnesium ions from hard water. Write chemical equations for the precipitation reactions of (a) magnesium ions with $Ca(OH)_2$, and (b) calcium ions with Na_2CO_3.

Teacher's Notes
How Hard Is Your Water?

Master Materials List *(for a class of 30 students working in pairs)*

Buffer solution, pH 10, 100 mL

Calmagite indicator solution, 0.05%, 50 mL

Distilled or deionized water

EDTA solution, 0.0075 M, 250 mL*

Standard solutions, 60, 120, and 180 ppm $CaCO_3$, 200 mL each

Tap water, pond or river water, pool water, etc.

Beral-type pipets, thin-stem, 30

Microtip, Beral-type pipets, 15

Reaction plates, 24-well, 15

Syringes, 3-mL, 15

Toothpicks, plastic (to stir), 75

Paper

Wash bottles, 15

Prepared from ethylenediaminetetraacetic acid, disodium salt, dihydrate. See the Preparation of Solutions section.

Preparation of Solutions *(for a class of 30 students working in pairs)*

Buffer Solution, pH 10: This is an ammonia/ammonium chloride buffer. Dissolve 0.64 g of ammonium chloride in about 50 mL of distilled or deionized water. Measure and add 5.7 mL of concentrated ammonium hydroxide solution (14.8 M), and stir to mix. Dilute the solution to 100 mL with water.

Calmagite solution, 0.05%: Dissolve 0.05 g of Calmagite in 100 mL of distilled or deionized water.

EDTA Solution, 0.0075 M: Add 0.70 g of EDTA disodium salt dihydrate ($C_{10}H_{14}N_2Na_2O_8 \cdot 2H_2O$) to about 100 mL of distilled or deionized water in a volumetric flask or graduated cylinder. Stir to dissolve and then dilute to 250 mL with water.

Standard Solution, 180 ppm $CaCO_3$: Dissolve 425 mg of reagent grade calcium nitrate tetrahydrate [$Ca(NO_3)_2 \cdot 4H_2O$] in 1 L of distilled or deionized water in a volumetric flask. To prepare 120 ppm standard solution, dilute 167 mL of the 180 ppm standard to 250 mL with distilled water. To prepare 60 ppm standard solution, dilute 83.3 mL of the 180 ppm standard to 250 mL with distilled water.

Safety Precautions

The pH 10 buffer solution is a body tissue irritant and is mildly toxic by ingestion. The solution may release harmful vapors—do not breathe the fumes. Avoid contact of all chemicals with eyes and skin. Wear chemical splash goggles, chemical-resistant gloves, and a chemical-resistant apron. Please review current Material Safety Data Sheets for additional safety, handling, and disposal information. Remind students to wash hands thoroughly with soap and water before leaving the lab.

Disposal

Please consult your current *Flinn Scientific Catalog/Reference Manual* for general guidelines and specific procedures governing the disposal of laboratory waste. The waste solutions may be rinsed down the drain with plenty of excess water according to Flinn Suggested Disposal Method #26b.

The molar mass of EDTA disodium salt dihydrate is 372.25 g/mol.

Lab Hints

- The lab work for this experiment can easily be completed in one 50-minute class period. Microscale titrations have several advantages for both the teacher and students compared to conventional titrations. For the teacher, the amounts of chemicals and the preparation time are greatly reduced, and disposal problems are minimized. For students, the procedure is fast and easy to perform, and so it is possible to carry out multiple trials for each sample. Using calibration standards (reference solutions) and a standard graph gives accuracy and precision results comparable to conventional titrations.

- Drop size is the most important variable affecting the reproducibility and reliability of microscale titrations. Consistent drop volumes are easily achieved using the microtip pipets described in the *Master Materials Guide* at the end of this book (Catalog No. AP1517). Proper technique is very important. The pipet should be held vertically above a reaction well, and any air bubbles should be expelled from the pipet stem before the EDTA is added to a reaction well.

- Microtip pipets may be prepared by "drawing out" standard thin-stem pipets (Catalog No. AP1444). Hold the bulb of a thin stem pipet in one hand, with the thumb and index finger positioned at the point where the drawn out portion of the stem should begin. With the free hand, wrap the exposed portion of the stem around the index finger. Gently stretch the stem to lengthen it about 3 inches, then cut the drawn-out stem to the desired length.

- The most common metal-ion indicator for EDTA titrations is EBT (Eriochrome Black T). On the microscale level, we found that calmagite gave a sharper and more distinct endpoint than EBT. Calmagite is blue in basic solution, but the complex of calmagite with calcium or magnesium ions is pink in basic solution.

- Using a color standard to identify the endpoint improves accuracy in the titrations. The color change is gradual, going from pink through purple to clear blue. The endpoint occurs at the point where there is no more pink present. Students who are colorblind will have a difficult time recognizing the pink–purple–blue color transitions.

- If there is a swimming pool in the school, talk with the swimming pool supervisor about having the chemistry students perform the water hardness test on the pool water. The recommended water hardness level for swimming pools and spas is 200–300 ppm. Compare the results obtained in the lab with those obtained poolside using typical "dip and read" test papers or methods. Also, schedule an in-house field trip to the pool to learn about the routine tests used to monitor pool chemistry and water quality: Chlorine, pH, Alkalinity, Total Dissolved Solids, Cyanuric Acid, Copper, and Iron.

- This experiment can easily be adapted into an inquiry-based lab. Challenge students to develop an efficient and economical method for softening hard water (>200 ppm) to an acceptable level for use in beverages (<50 ppm) using an ion-exchange resin. An appropriate resin is available from Flinn Scientific (Catalog No. Z0001).

Teaching Tips

- The recommended hardness level for pools and spas and other water uses is 200–300 ppm. Soft water is acidic and corrosive and has a tendency to dissolve or leach metals such as iron, copper, and lead from pipes and plumbing.

- The three principal ions that contribute to water hardness are calcium, magnesium, and iron. While there are no national, state or local standards for calcium and magnesium in drinking water, the EPA recommends a limit of 0.3 mg/L for the concentration of iron in drinking water. This is a recommended value and is not legally enforceable.

- Set up a collaborative classroom research project. Using the Internet, look up typical surface water, groundwater, or municipal water hardness levels in major cities or geographic areas for every state. Plot the data on a large map of the United States using a color-coded system for the USGS water hardness categories (see the *Background* section). Analyze the resulting national map in terms of geographic features and properties. Although about 85% of the country has hard water, there are wide variations depending on geography. New England and the Pacific Northwest generally have soft water, while very hard water (≥1000 ppm) is common in many areas of the Southwest such as Texas, New Mexico, Arizona, and Utah.

Answers to Pre-Lab Questions *(Student answers will vary.)*

1. What is the charge on the EDTA anion in strongly basic solution (pH 10)? What is the overall charge on the *complex ion* when a Ca^{2+} or Mg^{2+} ion is bound to EDTA?

   EDTA has a –4 charge in basic solution. The resulting Ca^{2+}–EDTA complex ion has a –2 charge.

2. The metal-ion indicator in an EDTA titration must bind to metal ions less strongly than EDTA does. Explain what would happen if the reverse were true.

   If a metal ion bonded more strongly to the indicator than to EDTA, EDTA would not displace the indicator from the Ca^{+2}–Ind complex ion at the endpoint. The endpoint would not be visible because there would be no color change.

3. A standard solution was prepared by dissolving 200 mg of calcium chloride ($CaCl_2$) in one liter of water. Calculate the equivalent water hardness for this standard solution in terms of ppm $CaCO_3$.

   Convert the concentration of calcium chloride to moles per liter, and then calculate the equivalent mass for the same number of moles of calcium carbonate.

$$\frac{0.200 \text{ g } CaCl_2}{1 \text{ L}} \times \frac{1 \text{ mole}}{110.98 \text{ g } CaCl_2} \times \frac{100.08 \text{ g } CaCO_3}{1 \text{ mole}} = \frac{0.180 \text{ g } CaCO_3}{1 \text{ L}} = 180 \text{ ppm}$$

Teacher Notes

Sample Data

Student data will vary.

Data Table

Sample	Number of Drops of EDTA Added			
	Trial 1	**Trial 2**	**Trial 3**	**Average**
Tap Water	28	30	28	29
Standard Solution (60 ppm CaCO$_3$)	7	7	7	7
Standard Solution (120 ppm CaCO$_3$)	13	13	14	13
Standard Solution (180 ppm CaCO$_3$)	19	19	19	19
Other (Pool Water)	33	33	31	32

Answers to Post-Lab Questions *(Student answers will vary.)*

1. Graph the titration results for the *standard solutions:* Plot the average number of drops of EDTA added on the *y*-axis versus water hardness in ppm CaCO$_3$ on the *x*-axis. Using a ruler or straight-edge, draw a best-fit straight line through the origin and the data points.

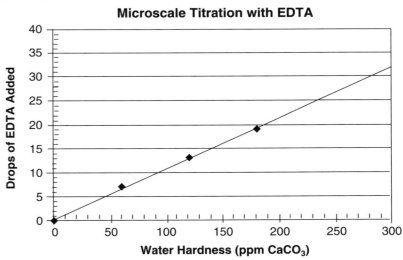

2. (a) Why is the origin included in this line? (b) Explain in principle how this graph can be used to determine the water hardness in an "unknown" sample.

   (a) The origin (0,0) should be included in the best-fit straight line because when the water hardness is zero, there are no calcium ions to react with any EDTA.

   (b) The standard graph may be used as a "calibration curve" to determine the equivalent concentration of calcium ions in hard water. The water hardness level is determined by finding the concentration on the x-axis corresponding to the number of drops of EDTA added to the unknown.

3. Using the graph, determine the water hardness in ppm $CaCO_3$ for tap water and any other water samples analyzed. Classify the hardness level: soft water, hard water, very hard, etc.

The water hardness levels were 270 ppm for tap water (very hard water) and 300 ppm for pool water.

4. A sample of pool water was analyzed by EDTA titration using a buret:

Volume of water tested   50.0 mL

Concentration of EDTA   0.010 M

Volume of EDTA added   15.4 mL

Calculate (a) the number of moles of EDTA added at the endpoint; (b) the equivalent mass of calcium carbonate in the pool water that reacted with EDTA; and (c) the water hardness level in parts per million (1 ppm = 1 mg $CaCO_3$/L).

(a) $0.0154\ L \times 0.010\ moles/L = 1.5 \times 10^{-4}\ moles\ EDTA$

(b) $1.5 \times 10^{-4}\ moles\ EDTA \times \dfrac{1\ mole\ Ca^{2+}}{1\ mole\ EDTA} \times \dfrac{100.08\ g\ CaCO_3}{1\ mole} = 0.015\ g\ CaCO_3$

(c) $\dfrac{0.015\ g \times 1000\ mg/g}{0.050\ L} = 300\ mg/L = 300\ ppm$ (2 significant figures)

5. Many municipal water treatment plants use lime [$Ca(OH)_2$] and soda ash (Na_2CO_3) to chemically remove calcium and magnesium ions from hard water. Write chemical equations for the precipitation reactions of (a) magnesium ions with $Ca(OH)_2$, and (b) calcium ions with Na_2CO_3.

(a) $Mg^{2+}(aq) + Ca(OH)_2(aq) \rightarrow Mg(OH)_2(s) + Ca^{2+}(aq)$

(b) $Ca^{2+}(aq) + Na_2SO_4(aq) \rightarrow CaSO_4(s) + 2Na^+(aq)$

Air Pollution Investigation
Air Quality

Teacher Notes

Introduction

How clean is the air you breathe? How does the air look, taste, feel or smell? What are some of the possible impurities in air? This laboratory activity examines several tests that can be performed to investigate air pollution and air quality.

Concepts

- Air pollution and air quality
- Particulates in air
- Combustion products
- Acid rain

Background

The major components of dry, pollution-free air are nitrogen (78%), oxygen (20.95%), argon (0.934%), and carbon dioxide (0.0314%). Air also contains trace quantities of neon, ammonia, helium, methane, and krypton. Air pollution results when additional or foreign substances that may affect living organisms are added to the atmosphere. Both natural and artificial (man-made) sources and activities contribute to air pollution, and air pollution is generally the most widespread and noticeable type of pollution. In 2005, about 140 million tons of pollutants were released into the atmosphere in the United States as a result of human activity.

There are five major classes of air pollutants—particulate materials, sulfur oxides, nitrogen oxides, carbon monoxide, and volatile organic compounds.

Particulate materials, also known as aerosols, are defined as any group of liquid droplets or solid materials suspended in air. Examples of particulate matter in air include dust, lint, smoke, pollen, ash, dirt, as well as many other suspended materials. Particulates are often the most visible and noticeable type of air pollution, and high levels of particulates in the air can be harmful to many living organisms. Globally, natural sources of particulate matter in the air account for more than ten times the particulates released from human sources. In many cities, however, more than 90% of suspended particulate matter in the air results from human activities.

Sulfur oxides are present in the air from both natural and human sources. Volcanoes, sea spray, dust from dry soils, and other natural events or processes are the major contributors of sulfur oxides into the atmosphere. The main form of sulfur oxides originating from human activities is sulfur dioxide (SO_2), which comes from the combustion of coal and oil and smelting or processing of ores. Sulfur dioxide is a colorless, corrosive gas that is a constituent of smog. It is toxic by inhalation and poses a significant health hazard to humans. Sulfur trioxide (SO_3), which is obtained by the further reaction of SO_2 with oxygen, combines with water in the atmosphere to make sulfuric acid, a strong acid that is a major component of acid rain (Equation 1).

$$SO_3 + H_2O \rightarrow H_2SO_4 \qquad \qquad \textit{Equation 1}$$

In the United States, the amount of pollutants released into the air has trended downward very significantly since 1970, when the first comprehensive Clean Air Act was passed. The production of the five major classes of air pollutants has decreased by more than 50% from 1970 through 2005 (from 300 million tons per year to 140 million tons).

Nitrogen oxides are released into the atmosphere mainly from the burning of fossil fuels. High-temperature combustion converts nitrogen-containing compounds in fuels as well as nitrogen gas in the air to nitrogen oxides. Motor vehicle emissions and electric utility plants are the principal sources of nitrogen oxide pollution. Nitrogen dioxide (NO_2) is a toxic, reddish brown gas and a respiratory irritant. It is primarily responsible for the brownish haze that hangs over many of the world's largest cities due to air pollution. Nitrogen oxides are very reactive in the air. In the presence of sunlight, for example, nitrogen dioxide undergoes a photochemical reaction to produce ozone (Equation 2). High levels of nitrogen oxides in the atmosphere are associated, therefore, with high ozone levels. Nitrogen dioxide also undergoes further oxidation and combines with moisture in the air to produce nitric acid (Equation 3).

$$NO_2 + O_2 \rightarrow NO + O_3 \qquad \textit{Equation 2}$$

$$2NO_2 + \tfrac{1}{2}O_2 + H_2O \rightarrow 2HNO_3 \qquad \textit{Equation 3}$$

Natural rainwater and other forms of precipitation are slightly acidic, with an average pH of 5.5. This natural acidity is due to carbonic acid (H_2CO_3), the weak acid obtained when carbon dioxide in the air combines with water (Equation 4).

$$CO_2 + H_2O \rightarrow H_2CO_3 \qquad \textit{Equation 4}$$

The presence of strong acids in the air can significantly increase the acidity of rain and other forms of precipitation. Rain that is acidic due to the presence of strong acids such as sulfuric acid and nitric acid in the atmosphere is called *acid rain*. In some areas of the United States, pH levels as low as 2.5 have been recorded for acid rain. Acidic rainfall causes chronic acidity in lakes and streams, which puts large amounts of stress on aquatic life (water becomes unsuitable for many organisms when the pH drops below 5–6). Many lakes in the United States have become so acidic that fish and other organisms that used to flourish have disappeared. The changes may be gradual at first, as snails, crayfish, insect larvae, and young fish are affected. This is followed by a domino effect that threatens ecological diversity and disturbs the entire ecosystem. Acid rain washes away essential nutrients from the soil, reducing soil quality, and can also cause direct harm to plants by damaging leaves and preventing the germination of seeds. On a more visible though less life-threatening level, acid rain erodes artwork and buildings and causes heavy damage to statues.

Carbon monoxide is a colorless, odorless gas that is highly toxic to humans and other organisms. It is present in the atmosphere mainly from the incomplete combustion of fossil fuels. If an internal combustion engine does not have the proper mix of fuel and air, carbon monoxide is formed instead of carbon dioxide (Equations 5 and 6). Carbon monoxide inhibits respiration in animals by competing with oxygen for the binding sites on hemoglobin. Every year, about one billion tons of carbon monoxide are released into the air from the exhaust vapors of cars, trucks, and other vehicles.

Complete combustion: $\qquad C_8H_{16} + 12O_2 \rightarrow 8CO_2 + 8H_2O \qquad \textit{Equation 5}$

Incomplete combustion: $C_8H_{16} + 11O_2 \rightarrow 6CO_2 + 2CO + 8H_2O \qquad \textit{Equation 6}$

Teacher Notes

Volatile organic compounds (VOC) are organic chemicals that persist in the atmosphere as gases. Plants are the largest source of volatile organic compounds in the air. In addition to natural sources of VOC, synthetic organic chemicals such as toluene, benzene, phenols, and chloroform are released into the atmosphere as the result of human activity. The major source of VOC production from human activities is the evaporation of gasoline at gas stations.

Experiment Overview

The purpose of this activity is to investigate the sources and effects of air pollution in the environment and to test the local air quality. The amount of particulate matter in the air will be measured using a week-long sampling protocol. The properties of the combustion products that contribute to air pollution and the level of acidic gases in the air will be studied using bromthymol blue indicator. (Bromthymol blue is an acid–base indicator that is yellow when the pH is <6.0, blue when the pH is >7.6, and green in neutral solution, pH = 7.) The effects of acid rain on common building materials also will be examined.

Pre-Lab Questions

1. Identify the major class of air pollutant most likely to be affected by each event or activity listed below, and state whether the event would increase or decrease the level of pollution.

    a. A volcano erupting
    b. Burning high-sulfur coal
    c. Fewer people smoking cigarettes
    d. Driving an old car
    e. Turning the thermostat up to 76 °F in summer
    f. Adding vapor recovery on gasoline pumps
    g. Adding a nitrogen-containing additive to gasoline
    h. Strong winds blowing into the area after a drought
    i. Adding a scrubber to a factory smokestack

2. Based on where you live, which class of pollutants probably contributes more to local air pollution—particulates or sulfur and nitrogen oxides?

3. Name some good locations for the particulate matter capture slides in Part A.

Materials

Bromthymol blue indicator solution, 3 mL	Matches, 1 book
Building materials, 2 pieces of each material	Microscope slide(s)
Distilled or deionized water	pH paper
"Unpolluted rainwater," 4 mL	Reaction plate, 24-well
"Simulated acid rain solution," 4 mL	Ruler
Yeast suspension, 2 mL	Test tube with cap (or stopper)
Beral-type pipets, 3	Stereoscope (optional)
Label, adhesive	Syringe, 10-mL
Magnifying glass	Tubing, 2-inch piece
Marking pen	Wash bottle

Safety Precautions

The acid rain solution is toxic by ingestion and inhalation and is corrosive to skin and eyes. Please observe all normal laboratory safety guidelines. Wear goggles or safety glasses whenever working with chemicals, heat or glassware in the laboratory. Wash hands thoroughly with soap and water before leaving the lab.

Procedure

Part A. Particulates in the Air

1. Place a label, *sticky side up,* on the microscope slide. This may be done by curling two of the outside edges of the label down so the label will stick to the slide. Label the slide with your initials.

2. Choose a location, inside or outside, to place the slide. For best results, choose a site that is exposed to the air, elevated off the ground, and sheltered from the rain, if possible. In the data table, describe where the slide was placed, *e.g.,* inside the classroom by a window, in a tree, near the corner of the school building, etc. *Note:* Discuss possible sample locations with your classmates, so that many different sites can be tested.

3. Leave the slide in the test location for seven days.

4. After seven days, collect the microscope slide and examine the label using a magnifying glass. Observe the color, texture, and appearance of the most common particulates, and also note if there were any specific problems with the collection, *e.g.,* a twig fell across sampling square. Record all observations in the data table.

5. Measure and draw two 1-cm squares on the label. Using the magnifying glass, count the number of particulates in each square (look for white as well as dark specs). Count each square twice and record the average particle count for each square in the data table.

6. Determine the average number of particles for the two squares and record the overall result (particles per square centimeter) in the data table.

7. (*Optional*) Examine the microscope slide using a stereoscope at 20X power.

Part B. Combustion Products and Air Pollution

8. Fill a medium-size test tube about two-thirds full with distilled water. Using a Beral-type pipet, add 20 drops of bromthymol blue to the water and swirl to mix the solution.

9. Observe the initial color of the indicator solution in the test tube and record the color in the data table.

10. Light a match and drop it *while it is still burning* into the indicator solution in the test tube, and then immediately cap or stopper the test tube. Try to capture all of the smoke from the match in the test tube.

11. Swirl the solution in the test tube until the smoke dissolves.

12. Observe and record the color of the solution and estimate the pH: Yellow, pH <6.0; green, pH 7; blue, pH >7.6).

To get a good picture of the range of particulates in the air, we recommend that each group set up 2–3 microscope slides in Part A. This will give more information of variations in local air quality and air pollution.

Teacher Notes

13. Rinse the test tube twice with distilled water, and then refill the tube about two-thirds full with distilled water.

14. Using a Beral-type pipet, add 20 drops of bromthymol blue to the water. Swirl the test tube to mix the solution. Observe the initial color—it should be the same as in step 8.

15. Attach a 2-inch piece of rubber tubing to the end of a syringe as seen in Figure 1. Fill the syringe with outside air.

16. Depress the plunger of the syringe to force the air through the tubing (out of the syringe) and into the solution in the test tube.

Figure 1.

17. Repeat steps 15 and 16 a total of *ten times*. Observe and record the color of the indicator solution and the pH in the data table.

18. Rinse the syringe, rubber tubing, and test tube with distilled water.

Part C. Acid Rain

19. Obtain the building materials to be tested from your instructor. Some of the possible building materials are marble or chalk, copper wire, iron nails, and brick nuggets.

20. Place a small sample of each building material into two separate wells of a 24-well reaction plate. Record the well numbers for each building material in the data table.

21. Using a Beral-type pipet, place 20 drops of "unpolluted rain water" on one sample of each building material. Wait a few minutes and then record observations in the data table.

22. Using a Beral-type pipet, place 20 drops of "simulated acid rain" on the second sample of each building material. Wait a few minutes and then record observations in the data table.

23. Place about 1–2 mL of an active yeast suspension in an empty well on the reaction plate.

24. Using a Beral-type pipet, add 20 drops of "simulated acid rain" to the yeast suspension. Wait a few minutes and then record observations in the data table.

25. Place 20 drops of "unpolluted rainwater" in a clean well and 20 drops of the "simulated acid rain" in a different clean well. Measure the pH of each rain sample using pH paper and record the results in the data table.

Name: _____

Class/Lab Period: _____

Air Pollution Investigation

Data Table

Part A. Particulates in the Air

Location of slide	
Observations of particulate materials	
Count 1 (1 cm²)	
Count 2 (1 cm²)	
Average number of particulates per square cm	

Part B. Combustion Products and Air Pollution

Initial color and pH of distilled water and bromthymol blue indicator solution	
Color and pH after smoke dissolved in water	
Color and pH after outside air was blown through solution	

Part C. Acid Rain

	Simulated Acid Rain	Unpolluted Rainwater
Building Material _____		
Building Material _____		
Yeast Suspension		
pH		

Teacher Notes

Post-Lab Questions *(Use a separate sheet of paper to answer the following questions.)*

Part A. Particulates in the Air

1. Total particle counts of 100 to 500 per square centimeter indicate slight particle pollution. Values over 500 particles per square centimeter correspond to high particle air pollution. (a) Did your test area have low or high particle pollution? (b) Could you identify some of the particulates in the local air sample?

2. Give examples of possible sources of particulate air pollution in your test area.

3. Compare results obtained by your classmates for different sample locations. Which location(s) had the highest number of particulates?

4. Which location(s) had the largest and the smallest particulates?

5. Which location(s) had the greatest variety of particulates?

Part B. Combustion Products and Air Pollution

6. Describe what happened to the solution and the atmosphere above the solution when the match fell into the water.

7. After the indicator solution was shaken to dissolve all of the combustion gases (smoke), what was the effect on the pH indicator? What does this color change indicate?

8. What compounds produced by the burning match are responsible for the observed pH change?

9. After the outside air was bubbled through the bromthymol blue indicator solution, what was the effect on the indicator? What does this color change indicate?

10. What are some possible sources of any pH changes observed with outdoor air?

Part C. Acid Rain

11. What effect did simulated acid rain have on each type of building material?

12. Why was each building material tested with both unpolluted rainwater and simulated acid rain?

13. What does this experiment demonstrate about the effect of acid rain on buildings and statues in large cities or major metropolitan areas?

14. What effect did simulated acid rain have on the yeast culture?

Teacher's Notes
Air Pollution Investigation

Master Materials List *(for a class of 30 students working in pairs)*

Bromthymol blue indicator solution, 0.04%, 50 mL

Distilled water, "Unpolluted rainwater," 100 mL

Hydrochloric acid, "Simulated acid rain," 0.001 M, 100 mL

Building materials*

    Marble chips (limestone), $CaCO_3$, 30 g

    Chalk (calcium carbonate), 30 g

    Iron nails, 15

    Copper wire, 15

    Brick pieces, 15

Yeast suspension, 50 mL

Beral-type pipets or eyedroppers, 45

Labels, adhesive, ½ × 1¾, 50–80,
    (Avery brand, 5126)

Choose 2–3 building materials from the list.

Magnifying glasses, 15

Marking pens, 5

Matches, 15 books

Microscope slides, 50–80

pH test paper, pH 3–6, 30 strips

Reaction plates, 24-well, 15

Rulers, metric, 15

Test tubes with caps, 15

Stereoscope (optional)

Syringes, 10-mL, 15

Tubing, plastic or latex,
    ⅛″ I.D., 3 ft (cut into
    2-inch sections)

Wash bottles, 15

Preparation of Materials *(for a class of 30 students working in pairs)*

Bromthymol Blue Indicator Solution, 0.04%: Dissolve 0.04 g of bromthymol blue in 100 mL of distilled or deionized water.

Unpolluted Rainwater: Use distilled or deionized water

Simulated Acid Rain: Use dilute 0.001 or 0.0001 M hydrochloric acid (pH = 3–4). To prepare, dilute 1 mL of 1 M hydrochloric acid to 1000 mL with distilled or deionized water.

Yeast suspension: Prepare a yeast solution by adding a packet of Baker's yeast to 100 mL of warm tap water. Add about 5 g of table sugar as a nutrient. Prepare fresh so the suspension will be very active.

Safety Precautions

Hydrochloric acid solution is toxic by ingestion and inhalation and is corrosive to skin and eyes. Wear goggles or safety glasses whenever working chemicals, heat or glassware in the laboratory. Please review current Material Safety Data Sheets for additional safety, handling, and disposal information. Remind students to wash hands thoroughly with soap and water before leaving the lab.

Disposal

Please consult your current *Flinn Scientific Catalog/Reference Manual* for general guidelines and specific procedures governing the disposal of laboratory waste. The "simulated acid rain" solution may be rinsed down the drain with plenty of excess water according to Flinn Suggested Disposal Method #26b.

Teacher Notes

Lab Hints

- The laboratory work for Parts B and C can easily be completed in a typical 50-minute lab period. For best results, set up and place the slides needed for Part A at the end of one lab period, then collect the slides and count the number of particles on the slides during the next week's lab period. Depending on air quality, 5–7 days is usually required to collect enough particles to measure. At least one week is usually needed if indoor sites are sampled. For outdoor sample sites, a shorter collection time may be sufficient.

- Remind students to draw two random 1-cm squares on the particulate collection slide. Deciding what is a particulate and how many particulates are in the square is difficult. If two students count the same particulates slide, then a more accurate count may be obtained.

- Have students count the number of particulates using a magnifying glass and then a 20X stereoscope. The number of particulates is usually five to ten times greater when the particulates are counted using a microscope.

- Encourage students to place their slides for Part A in a variety of locations. Allow students to take their slides out of the classroom to sample the total particulates in or around the school and their homes. Compile class data and compare results.

- The main components of the match head are red phosphorus and other phosphorus compounds, sulfur, and potassium compounds. The smoke from the match consists of phosphorus oxides and sulfur oxides, and may be compared to the fumes emitted by some types of factories.

- When collecting air samples for Part B, encourage students to collect a gallon zipper-lock bag of air from behind a school bus, the sidewalk next to a busy street, or the area next to the school's heating and cooling unit's exhaust.

- Consider preparing more than one concentration of "simulated acid rain" to compare the effect of different pH levels on the building materials and the rate of damage. Collect rainwater and test the pH of local rainwater.

- The effect of acid rain on living organisms in an ecosystem is very complex. Reducing the pH of a pond or lake leads to changes in the concentration of various metals and nutrients in the water. Increased concentrations of aluminum ions in acidic lakes and streams are responsible for killing off fish. Changing nutrient levels promote the overgrowth of algae and fungal mats and reduce the amount of dissolved oxygen in the water. The experiment with the yeast suspension demonstrates the effect of acid on one living organism.

Teaching Tips

- Contact local manufacturing facilities to arrange a tour of their plants. Discuss the steps that the company takes to reduce the amount of air pollution coming from their facility.

- Visit the United States Environmental Protection Agency's (EPA) Web site at www.epa.gov/airtrends for further information on air pollution and how various government programs or policies have impacted trends in air quality in recent years.

Answers to Pre-Lab Questions *(Student answers will vary.)*

1. Identify the major class of air pollutant most likely to be affected by each event or activity listed below, and state whether the event would increase or decrease the level of pollution.

a. A volcano erupting	*Particulate materials*	*Increase*
b. Burning high-sulfur coal	*Sulfur oxides*	*Increase*
c. Fewer people smoking cigarettes	*Particulate materials*	*Decrease*
d. Driving an old car	*Carbon monoxide*	*Increase*
e. Turning the thermostat up to 76 °F in summer	*Sulfur/nitrogen oxides*	*Decrease*
f. Adding vapor recovery on gasoline pumps	*Volatile organics*	*Decrease*
g. Adding a nitrogen-containing additive to gasoline	*Nitrogen oxides*	*Increase*
h. Strong winds blowing into the area after a drought	*Particulate materials*	*Increase*
i. Adding a scrubber to a factory smokestack	*Sulfur/nitrogen oxides*	*Decrease*

2. Based on where you live, which class of pollutants probably contributes more to local air pollution— particulates or sulfur and nitrogen oxides?

   Answers will vary. In rural areas, particulate materials may be high due to dust storms, pollen, and smoke from burning wood. In urban areas, carbon monoxide and sulfur and nitrogen oxides are generally higher due to motor vehicle emissions.

3. Name some good locations for the particulate matter capture slides in Part A.

   Answers will vary. Encourage creative areas to capture unique air pollution sources such as buses, factories, and agricultural fields.

Teacher Notes

Sample Data

Student data will vary.

Data Table

Part A. Particulates in the Air	
Location of slide	Slide was placed on a shelf in the classroom.
Observations of particulate materials	Many small particulates were seen. Most of the particulates were black in color. Some particles looked like dust and fiber.
Count 1 (1 cm^2)	50 particles
Count 2 (1 cm^2)	64 particles
Average number of particulates per square cm	57 particles/cm^2

Part B. Combustion Products and Air Pollution	
Initial color and pH of distilled water and bromthymol blue indicator solution	The solution was green, pH = 7.
Color and pH after smoke dissolved in water	The solution turned yellow. The pH was reduced to <6.0.
Color and pH after outside air was blown through solution	Results will vary.

Part C. Acid Rain

	Simulated Acid Rain	Unpolluted Rainwater
Building Material __Marble__	There is a lot of bubbling and a gas is produced.	No reaction
Building Material ___Iron___	A small amount of bubbling is observed.	No reaction
Yeast Suspension	The amount of bubbling decreases and soon stops.	Lots of bubbling as the yeast produce carbon dioxide.
pH	3.0	6.0

Answers to Post-Lab Questions *(Student answers will vary.)*   Teacher Notes

Part A. Particulates in the Air

1. Total particle counts of 100 to 500 per square centimeter indicate slight particle pollution. Values over 500 particles per square centimeter correspond to high particle air pollution. (a) Did your test area have low or high particle pollution? (b) Could you identify some of the particulates in the local air sample?

   Most indoor test areas had only slight particle pollution. Particles may have come from dust, clothes, natural fibers or from an open window or ventilation ducts.

2. Give examples of possible sources of particulate air pollution in your test area.

   Answers will vary depending on the location.

3. Compare results obtained by your classmates for different sample locations. Which location(s) had the highest number of particulates?

   The highest number of particulates came from a slide placed in the school bus garage.

4. Which location(s) had the largest and the smallest particulates?

   The largest particles came from a slide placed near an open field. The smallest particles came from the slides in the classroom.

5. Which location(s) had the greatest variety of particulates?

   A slide that was placed on a tree branch had the greatest variety of particles.

Part B. Combustion Products and Air Pollution

6. Describe what happened to the solution and the atmosphere above the solution when the match fell into the water.

   A lot of smoke was produced when the match went out. The atmosphere above the solution was cloudy with white smoke. The solution changed from green to yellow.

7. After the indicator solution was shaken to dissolve all of the combustion gases (smoke), what was the effect on the pH indicator? What does this color change indicate?

   The bromthymol blue indicator solution turn from an initial green color (pH = 7) to yellow when the match was dropped into the solution. The pH decreased to pH <6.

8. What compounds produced by the burning match are responsible for the observed pH changes?

   The match head contains some sulfur and phosphorus that underwent combustion to form phosphorus oxides and sulfur oxides. The oxides reacted with the water to form strong acids, which lowered the pH of the solution.

9. After the outside air was bubbled through the bromthymol blue indicator solution, what was the effect on the indicator? What does this color change indicate?

   The bromthymol blue indicator solution did not change color using outdoor air. It did change color from green to yellow-green when we tested air from behind a bus. These results indicate that the tested air does not contain high levels of nitrogen and sulfur oxides.

10. What are some possible sources of any pH changes observed with outdoor air?

    The outdoor air was not very polluted. However, air collected from behind a bus did give a color change (to yellow), probably due to carbon dioxide, carbon monoxide, sulfur oxides, and nitrogen oxides produced in the exhaust.

Part C. Acid Rain

11. What effect did simulated acid rain have on each type of building material?

    The simulated acid rain reacted with the marble chips and the metals. A reaction was observed due to either bubbles forming (on the marble and the iron) or a discoloration of the solution (iron).

12. Why was each building material tested with both unpolluted rainwater and simulated acid rain?

    The unpolluted water was a control to make sure that the reaction was due to the acids in the acid rain and not the pure water.

13. What does this experiment demonstrate about the effect of acid rain on buildings and statues in large cities or major metropolitan areas?

    The simulated acid rain reacted with the marble which means that many marble or limestone buildings may be destroyed by acid rain. Copper and iron should not be used as building materials unless they are protected from acids.

14. What effect did simulated acid rain have on the yeast culture?

    After a few minutes, it appeared that the yeast culture was no longer active.

Build a Solar Cell
Photovoltaic Effect and Photosynthesis

Introduction

Solar energy, the conversion of sunlight to electricity, has enormous potential as a clean source of renewable energy to replace fossil fuels. Although solar energy has powered satellites and spacecraft for almost 50 years, it accounts for less than 1% of electricity generated in the United States today. An important factor limiting the use of solar energy is the trade-off between cost and efficiency. High-performance solar cells require large, high-purity silicon crystals, which are very expensive to produce. Less expensive forms of silicon are not as efficient. Recently, a new type of photovoltaic cell has been developed that promises a better balance between cost and efficiency. Dye-sensitized solar cells mimic the process that occurs in photosynthesis to harvest sunlight and convert it to electricity.

Concepts

- Photovoltaic cell
- Photoelectrochemical cell
- Photoelectric effect
- Semiconductor

Background

A solar cell, also called a photovoltaic cell, is a light-sensitive semiconductor device that uses the *photoelectric effect* to convert sunlight into electricity. A semiconductor is a material whose electrical conductivity increases with temperature or when irradiated with light. The increase in conductivity is due to electrons being promoted from the valence band to the conduction band. The energy difference is called the band gap energy and determines how much energy must be supplied for the material to conduct electricity.

Conventional solar cells contain a silicon diode as the semiconductor. The diode is created by joining n-type silicon (silicon doped with an impurity that has one more valence electron than silicon) to p-type silicon (silicon doped with an impurity that has one fewer valence electron than silicon). The different properties of the materials at the p–n junction give rise to a potential difference at the interface. Light striking the silicon surface excites electrons from the valence band to the conduction band and creates "electron-hole pairs." Electrons move toward the positive side of the junction, "electron holes" toward the negative side, and the resulting flow of electrons generates an electric current. The main factor limiting the use of solid-state solar cells is cost. In order to obtain maximum efficiency in the conversion of sunlight into electricity, large, high-purity silicon crystals are required. At the present time, both the raw material and the manufacturing costs are prohibitive for widespread residential use.

In 1991, Michael Grätzel of the Swiss Federal Institute of Technology in Lausanne, Switzerland, reported a new type of solar cell called a dye-sensitized solar cell (DSC). Since the first DSC prototype was demonstrated more than 10 years ago, the technology has been commercialized to build solar panels for roofs and buildings. The structure of a dye-sensitized solar cell separates the light-absorbing and electron-transfer functions of the solar cell, allowing both functions to be independently optimized.

This experiment is suitable for an advanced or honors-level class. The technology may be new and unfamiliar to students and the teacher alike. Please read all of the Teacher's Notes *section, beginning on page 60, before starting work on this activity.*

Dye-sensitized solar cells are *photoelectrochemical cells*. The anode is nanocrystalline titanium oxide, a wide band–gap semiconductor, and the cathode is carbon or platinum. An iodine/iodide electrolyte solution serves as a redox catalyst in the solar cell. Nanocrystalline titanium oxide (particle size 10–50 nm) is deposited as a thin film onto the surface of a conductive glass or polymer sheet. The coating is heated to anneal the titanium oxide particles and improve the electronic contact between the particles, and is then stained with a dye to make it sensitive to visible light. [The band gap energy of titanium oxide is about 3 eV, corresponding to ultraviolet light energy (about 400 nm). In the absence of a dye, ultraviolet light would be needed to initiate the photoelectric effect.] Using a nanocrystalline form of titanium oxide increases the effective surface area of the dye that is exposed to solar radiation and improves the efficiency of light absorption. The maximum possible voltage for this type of solar cell is about 0.9 V—this is the difference between the conduction band of TiO_2 and the standard reduction potential of iodine.

The function of the dye in a dye-sensitized solar cell is similar to the light-harvesting reaction of chlorophyll during photosynthesis. The dye absorbs visible light, which promotes an electron from the ground state to an excited state. The excited state electrons are transferred to the conduction band of titanium oxide, leaving oxidized dye molecules on the surface. The electrons migrate through the titanium oxide film and travel through the external circuit to the cathode. The dye is regenerated by accepting an electron from an iodide ion in the electrolyte solution. Iodide ions, acting as a redox catalyst, are regenerated by reduction of iodine at the cathode.

The components of a dye-sensitized solar cell are illustrated in the following schematic diagram (Figure 1), and the working principles are summarized in steps 1–6:

1) Dye molecule absorbs visible light.

2) An electron in the dye is promoted to a "photoexcited state" (S*).

3) S* transfers an electron into the conduction band (Fermi level, E_f) of TiO_2.

4) The oxidized dye accepts an electron from the redox catalyst (I^-).

5) Electrons migrate through the external circuit to the cathode.

6) Iodine is reduced to iodide at the cathode, thus regenerating the redox catalyst.

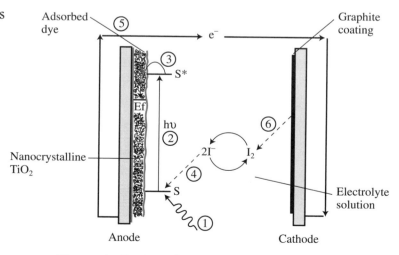

Figure 1. Design of a Dye-Sensitized Solar Cell.

Teacher Notes

Activity Overview

The purpose of this activity is to build a dye-sensitized solar cell (DSC) and measure its electrical characteristics. The DSC is built using conductive glass plates as supports for the anode and the cathode. The anode is nanocrystalline titanium oxide that is stained with a dye to absorb visible light, and the cathode is graphite. The cell is filled with an iodine/iodide electrolyte solution that acts as a redox catalyst. Students should work in groups of three or four.

Materials

Ethyl alcohol, 5 mL	Conductive glass, $1'' \times 3''$ plates, 2
Hibiscus dye solution, 25 mL	Cotton swab
Iodine/Potassium iodide electrolyte solution, I_2/KI in ethylene glycol, 1 mL	Forceps or tweezers
	Hot plate
Titanium oxide, TiO_2, nanocrystalline, 2 g	Lens paper
Nitric acid, 0.001 M, 25 mL	Microscope slide
Water, distilled or deionized, 200 mL	Mortar and pestle
Beaker, 150-mL	Multimeter w/alligator clip leads
Beral type pipets, 3	Overhead projector
Binder clips, 2	Paper towels
Candle, Tealight	Petri dish
Cardboard box "canopy"	Spatula
Ceramic pad	Stirring rod
	Transparent tape, Magic™

Safety Precautions

The solvent for the iodine/potassium iodide electrolyte solution is ethylene glycol, a combustible organic liquid. Ethylene glycol is toxic by ingestion. The iodine is irritating to skin and eyes. Nanocrystalline titanium oxide is a fine dust and may be harmful if inhaled. Avoid breathing the fine particle dust and avoid contact of all chemicals with eyes and skin. The surface of the hot plate will be very hot. Place a HOT sign in front of the plate to warn observers that the hot plate is on. Wear chemical splash goggles, chemical-resistant gloves, and a chemical-resistant apron. Wash hands thoroughly with soap and water before leaving the lab.

Preparation

1. Clean the conductive glass plates: Hold the plates with gloved hands or forceps and rinse with 2–3 mL of ethyl alcohol. Pat the plates dry with lens paper.

2. Identify the conducting sides of the conductive glass plates: Set the multimeter to ohms and place the multimeter probes on the surface of the glass. The conductive side will have a reading of 10–30 ohms. Place the glass plates *conductive side up* on a clean paper towel.

Procedure

Part A. Titanium Oxide Anode

1. Preheat the hot plate at a *medium setting* for use in steps 8–11.

2. Place 2 g of nanocrystalline titanium oxide in a clean mortar. Add 1 mL of 0.001 M nitric acid and grind the white powder to obtain a thick paste. Continue adding 1 mL of dilute nitric acid until a total of 3 mL of acid have been added and the titanium oxide suspension is milky white, smooth, and free-flowing. There should be no lumps or bubbles in the suspension. *Note:* This suspension may be shared between four groups of students.

3. Use a plastic spatula to scrape dry paste from the sides of the mortar back into the suspension, if needed. To prevent the suspension from drying out, store immediately in a capped bottle (preferably in the dark).

4. Using Magic™ transparent tape, tape a glass plate, conductive side up, to a clean surface with *two layers of tape,* as shown in Figure 2. The tape should mask about 5 mm of glass on each short side of the plate. (The tape will control the thickness of the titanium oxide coating.)

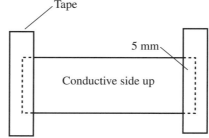

Figure 2.

5. Using a Beral pipet, add a thin line of TiO$_2$ suspension all the way across both the top and the bottom of the glass plate (Figure 3a).

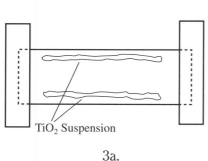

TiO$_2$ Suspension

3a.

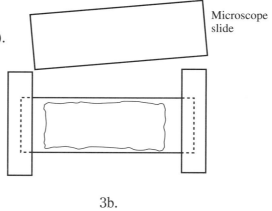

3b.

Figure 3. Coating the Anode with the Titanium Oxide.

6. With a clean microscope slide as a "squeegee," use the long, thin edge of the slide to draw the TiO$_2$ suspension smoothly across the glass and coat the entire exposed surface (Figure 3b). *Do not lift the slide off the glass.* If any uncoated areas remain, push the microscope slide back up to the top of the glass plate. (This whole process must be done quickly to avoid drying out the suspension before the surface is covered.)

7. When the TiO$_2$ coating is dry (about 1 minute), gently remove the tape from the sides of the coated plate. Be careful not to scratch or mar the coating.

Teacher Notes

8. Place the glass plate, *coated side up,* on the surface of the preheated hot plate (see step 1).

9. After about 5 minutes, the titanium oxide coating will turn light brown at the edges. Continue heating the plate until the off-white color of the titanium oxide coating is restored. This will take about 15 minutes. (Observe the plate during the heating process to avoid overheating the plate and cracking the glass.)

10. Turn off the hot plate and allow the glass plate to cool for 5 minutes before attempting to remove it from the surface.

11. Using metal tweezers or forceps, carefully remove the glass plate from the hot plate and place the glass plate on a ceramic pad to cool (about 15 minutes).

12. Stain the titanium oxide coating: Add about 20 mL of hibiscus dye solution to a Petri dish. Place the glass plate *coated side down* in the dye and allow it to soak for 10–15 minutes. (The coating should be dark purple with no white areas showing.)

13. Remove the dyed plate using tweezers or forceps and gently rinse the plate with a small amount of distilled water, followed by ethyl alcohol. Carefully blot dry with lens paper (do not rub).

Part B. Graphite Counterelectrode (Cathode)

14. Holding a second conductive glass plate with forceps, pass the plate, *conductive side down,* over a candle flame for 2–3 minutes to coat the conductive glass with a uniform layer of graphite. See Figure 4a. (The plate should look like it is coated with charcoal.)

15. Using a cotton swab, gently remove the graphite coating from two edges of the conductive glass plate (Figure 4b).

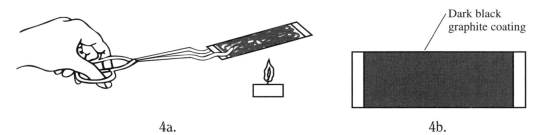

4a.

4b.

Figure 4. Preparing the Graphite Counterelectrode.

The dye solution (step 12) may be shared by several groups of students.

Part C. Assembling the Solar Cell

16. Lay the dyed titanium oxide electrode *face up* on a clean surface and place the graphite electrode *face down* on top of the titanium oxide electrode. Stagger the two plates so that part of the anode and part of the cathode will be exposed. Each plate extends out about 5 mm on either side of the glass "sandwich" and there is a clean exposed surface on each plate. (The exposed surfaces will be used as contact points for the alligator clip leads to the multimeter.) See Figure 5.

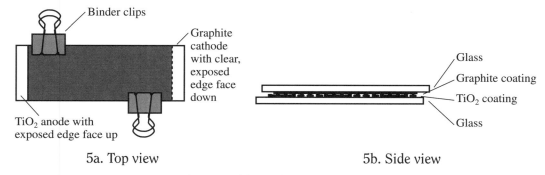

5a. Top view   5b. Side view

Figure 5. Assembling the Solar Cell "Sandwich."

17. Gently clamp the two electrodes together using small binder clips, as shown in Figure 5. Clamp only the edges of the plates, not all the way to the middle.

18. Carefully add 2–3 drops of iodine/potassium iodide electrolyte solution to one side of the solar cell "sandwich" in the area where the exposed glass meets the opposite electrode. The liquid will seep between the layers by capillary action.

19. Tilt the cell slightly and gently unclip and clip the binder clips to draw the liquid throughout the cell. It may also help to place a paper towel along the bottom edge of the cell.

20. Set the multimeter to measure the cell potential in volts (1–10 V). Connect the titanium oxide electrode (the anode) to the *negative* lead and the graphite electrode (the cathode) to the *positive* lead on the multimeter. (The titanium oxide is the anode and the graphite electrode is the cathode. Do NOT reverse the leads—a reverse bias may damage the cell.)

21. Measure and record the voltage of the solar cell under normal light illumination in the classroom.

22. Place the solar cell, photoanode side down, on the overhead projector stage. Measure and record the solar cell voltage when illuminated.

23. Place the solar cell in the dark (for example, under a cardboard box "canopy") and measure and record the dark solar cell voltage.

24. Set the multimeter to measure current in milliamps (1–20 mA). Connect the titanium oxide electrode to the negative lead and the graphite electrode to the positive lead.

25. Place the solar cell on the overhead projector and measure and record the current.

Teacher Notes

Name: _____

Class/Lab Period: _____

Build a Solar Cell Worksheet

Results Table

		Dyed Solar Cell (Prepared fresh)		Dyed Solar Cell (After 1 week)
Light Source	None	Classroom Light	Overhead Projector	Overhead Projector
Voltage				
Current				

Discussion Questions

1. What is the function of each of the following components in a dye-sensitized solar cell?

   (a) Titanium oxide

   (b) Conductive glass

   (c) Natural dye

   (d) Iodine/iodide electrolyte solution

2. What are the advantages of dye-sensitized solar cells compared to conventional solar cells? What are the possible disadvantages?

3. Predict how you would expect the voltage and the current produced by a DSC to change if the size of the solar cell were increased from 1″ × 3″ to 3″ × 3″.

Teacher's Notes
Build a Solar Cell

Technology

Master Materials List *(for a class of 24 students working in groups of three)*

Ethyl alcohol, 50 mL*

Hibiscus petals, dried, 4 g*

Iodine/Potassium iodide electrolyte
   solution, I_2/KI in ethylene glycol, 8 mL*

Titanium oxide, TiO_2, nanocrystalline, 4 g*

Nitric acid, 0.001 M, 200 mL*

Water, distilled or deionized

Beakers, 150-mL, 2

Beral-type pipets, 24

Binder clips, 16*

Candles, Tealight*

Cardboard box "canopy"

Ceramic pads, 2

Conductive glass, 1″ × 3″ plates, 16*

Cotton swabs, 8

Forceps or tweezers, 8

Hot plates, 2†

Lens paper*

Microscope slides, 8

Mortars and pestles, 2†

Multimeters w/alligator clip leads, 2†

Overhead projector†

Paper towels

Petri dishes, 8

Spatulas, 8

Stirring rods, 8

Transparent tape, Magic™

*Specialized components such as conductive glass plates, nanocrystalline TiO_2, and electrolyte solution are
   available as part of a laboratory kit available from Flinn Scientific (Build a Solar Cell, Catalog No. AP6916).
   Each kit contains enough materials to prepare four solar cells, including 2 g of nanocrystalline titanium oxide
   and 2 g of dried hibiscus.*

†Students may share hot plates, mortars and pestles, multimeters, and the overhead projector.

Preparation of Solutions *(for a class of 24 students working in groups of three)*

Nitric Acid, 0.001 M: Dilute 1 mL of 0.1 M nitric acid to 100 mL with distilled or deionized
water to prepare a 0.001 M nitric acid solution (pH 3). This solution will be used to prepare
the titanium oxide suspension and may also be used to store the titanium oxide coated plates,
if needed.

Hibiscus Dye Solution: Add 100 mL of distilled water to about 2 g of dried hibiscus in a
150-mL beaker and heat to boiling. Allow the mixture to steep for 15 minutes, then cool to
room temperature and filter. The concentrated dye solution may be stored in the refrigerator
overnight, if desired.

Safety Precautions

*The solvent for the iodine/potassium iodide electrolyte solution is ethylene glycol, a com-
bustible organic liquid. Ethylene glycol is toxic by ingestion. The iodine is irritating to skin
and eyes. Nanocrystalline titanium oxide is a fine dust and may be harmful if inhaled.
Avoid breathing the fine particle dust and avoid contact of all chemicals with eyes and skin.
The surface of the hot plate will be very hot. Place a HOT sign in front of the plate to warn
observers that the hot plate is on. Wear chemical splash goggles, chemical-resistant gloves,
and a chemical-resistant apron. Please consult current Material Safety Data Sheets for
additional safety, handling, and disposal information.*

Disposal

Please consult your current *Flinn Scientific Catalog/Reference Manual* for general guidelines and specific procedures governing the disposal of laboratory waste. Excess titanium oxide suspension may be disposed of in the trash according to Flinn Suggested Disposal Method #26a. Excess iodine/potassium iodide solution may be reduced with excess sodium thiosulfate solution and disposed of according to Flinn Suggested Disposal Method #26b. After disassembly, the solar cell components may be rinsed with water and then disposed of in the trash according to Flinn Suggested Disposal Method #26a.

Lab Hints and Teaching Tips

- The materials for this experiment are available as an activity kit from Flinn Scientific (Catalog No. AP6916).

- For greatest efficiency, prepare the titanium oxide suspension as well as the hibiscus dye extract the day before the cells will be made. The cells may then be prepared in assembly line fashion—plan on about two hours for Parts A–C. There are two good stopping points if the complete setup and demonstration cannot be completed at one time. The undyed, titanium oxide–coated anode may be stored completely submerged in a dilute nitric acid solution in the dark. (Do not store the dyed electrode—some of the dye will rinse off in the solvent.) The graphite coated plates may also be stored in any safe location where they will not be accidentally disturbed. Alternatively, the anode and cathode may be clamped together and stored in the dark before the electrolyte solution is added. Finally, Parts A and B may be done by different groups as part of a collaborative class project.

- The solar cells are reusable and may be stored for several weeks in the dark. The cell voltage will decrease during storage, but the cell current is fairly stable. The electrolyte layer may be replenished by adding a few more drops of electrolyte solution as needed to ensure complete coverage.

- Conductive glass is produced by depositing a thin, transparent coating of fluorine-doped tin oxide (SnO_2:F) on the glass by pyrolysis. Tin oxide is a wide–band–gap semiconductor.

- In a voltaic cell, the anode is considered the negative electrode, the cathode the positive electrode.

- In this experiment, the sensitizer dye is a naturally-occuring anthocyanin pigment isolated from dried hibiscus. Anthocyanins are highly colored pigments that are responsible for the red, blue, and purple colors in many different flowers and fruits. These pigments are normally present in all leaves but are usually masked by the green color of chlorophyll. In the fall, when the chlorophyll pigments become inactive, the red colors of the anthocyanins break through and are responsible for the bright orange and red fall foliage colors. The hibiscus extract prepared in this activity is a 1% solution—extraction of 2 g of dried hibiscus petals with 100 mL of water removes about 1 g of soluble substances. The absorption spectrum of a 1:10 diluted extract (approximately 0.1%) shows a strong absorbance maximum at 520 nm, as expected (Figure 6).

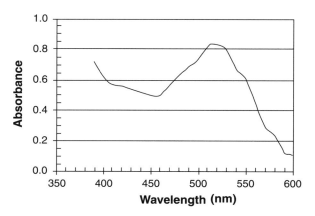

Figure 6. Visible Spectrum of Hibiscus Extract.

- Experiment with different dyes to see how they affect the solar cell. Extract fruits and flowers with water or ethyl alcohol and use the resulting dye solutions to stain the titanium oxide film. Nearly all fruits and flowers that are bright red, blue or purple contain a class of pigments or natural indicators called anthocyanins. Anthocyanins are derivatives of cyanidin with a varying numbers of hydroxyl (OH) and glucoside (OGl) groups attached to the aromatic rings in the structure (Figure 7).

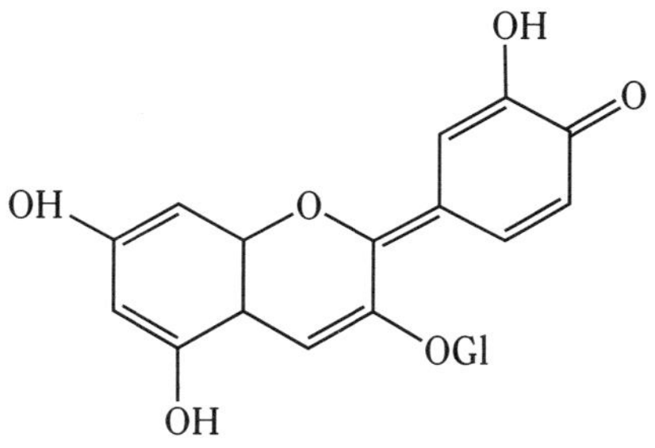

Figure 7. General Structure of Anthocyanin Dyes.

- Construct an undyed solar cell and compare its electrical properties versus a dye-sensitized solar cell. The band gap energy for titanium oxide is 3–3.2 eV, corresponding to long-wavelength ultraviolet light (400 nm). An undyed titanium oxide solar cell will therefore require ultraviolet light for photoinitiation. In our experience, the maximum cell voltage for an undyed solar cell was about 0.25 V in sunlight, as opposed to 0.45 V for a dye-sensitized solar cell on an overhead projector. Theoretically, the maximum cell voltage is equal to the voltage difference between the Fermi level of the semiconductor and the standard reduction potential of the redox catalyst. For titanium oxide and iodine, the theoretical cell voltage is 0.9–1.0 V.

Teacher Notes

- Connect two cells in series and measure the combined voltage and current. The voltage is additive when cells are connected in series. The current, however, does not change when cells are connected in series—the same current flows through each cell in the series. Connect two cells in parallel and measure the combined voltage and current. The current is additive when cells are connected in parallel. The voltage should be the average of the individual voltages of each cell in the parallel circuit. Optimum performance is usually obtained with a parallel–series circuit (Figure 8).

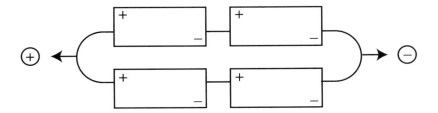

Figure 8. Parallel–Series Circuit.

Sample Data and Results

Student data will vary.

	Dyed Solar Cell (Prepared fresh)			Dyed Solar Cell (After 1 week)
Light Source	None	Classroom Light	Overhead Projector	Overhead Projector
Voltage	0.01 V	0.23 V	0.42 V	0.35 V
Current	N/A	0.23 mA	0.73 mA	0.71 mA

Answers to Discussion Questions

1. What is the function of each of the following components in a dye-sensitized solar cell?

   (a) Titanium oxide

   Titanium oxide is a semiconductor. Electrons are transferred from excited dye molecules and enter the conduction band of titanium oxide. The electrons then migrate from the anode to the cathode via an external circuit.

   (b) Conductive glass

   A conductive surface is needed for both electrodes to complete the external circuit for migration of electrons from the anode to the cathode through the solar cell.

   (c) Natural dye

   The dye absorbs visible light and acts as a "sensitizer" for the titanium oxide. Titanium oxide by itself does not absorb visible light.

   (d) Iodine/iodide electrolyte solution

   The iodine/iodide electrolyte solution acts as a redox catalyst to regenerate the reduced form of the dye at the anode.

2. What are the advantages of dye-sensitized solar cells compared to conventional solar cells? What are the possible disadvantages?

   Dye-sensitized solar cells do not require expensive, high-purity silicon for their manufature. However, DSC are not as efficient as conventional solar cells.

3. Predict how you would expect the voltage and the current produced by a DSC to change if the size of the solar cell were increased from 1″ × 3″ to 3″ × 3″.

   The voltage of a DSC is an intrinsic property of the materials used in the solar cell and thus should not depend on the size of the cell. The current of a DSC should increase as the size of the solar cell increases, because there is a greater flow of electrons. **Note to teachers:** *The current of a DSC is usually expressed in milliamps per square centimeter (mA/cm^2).*

Teacher Notes

Dissolved Oxygen Testing
Biochemical Oxygen Demand and Water Quality

Introduction

Without a critical supply of oxygen gas dissolved in water, fish and other aquatic organisms would drown. The amount of dissolved oxygen in water is one of the most important indicators of water quality and environmental health. How do environmental factors such as temperature, dissolved salts, and organic matter affect the level of dissolved oxygen?

Concepts

- Dissolved oxygen
- Winkler titration
- Biological oxygen demand
- Water quality

Background

Dissolved oxygen (DO) is the amount of gaseous oxygen, O_2, dissolved in a body of water. The most common units for measuring DO levels are milligrams of oxygen per liter of water (mg/L), or parts per million (ppm) O_2, where 1 ppm = 1 mg/L. Oxygen enters into the water by aeration, diffusion from air, and as a by-product of photosynthesis. In general, high flow rates or water turbulence will increase oxygen levels in water due to aeration. Slow moving or stagnant water usually has very low oxygen levels. Oxygen levels also change throughout the day as a result of photosynthesis, usually peaking in late afternoon. The amount of oxygen that will dissolve in water depends on temperature and pressure, and is very sensitive to environmental conditions.

Dissolved oxygen is inversely related to temperature—as the water temperature increases, the amount of oxygen that can dissolve decreases. In the summer, extremely warm water temperatures may result in very low dissolved oxygen. Typical environmental factors that affect DO levels include the amount of organic matter or waste from decaying vegetation, the presence of nitrates, phosphates, and other nutrients, and the concentration of electrolytes such as Na^+, Ca^{2+}, Mg^{2+}, Cl^-, and HCO_3^- ions. Dissolved oxygen is one of the most important indicators of the overall health of a body of water. When water contains a large amount of oxygen, the quality of the water is generally very good. Water with consistently low dissolved oxygen levels (<3–4 ppm) is extremely stressful to aquatic organisms and may harbor only a few species adapted to such conditions. DO levels less than 2 ppm will not support fish life.

The relationship between the amount of dissolved oxygen in water and water quality is usually expressed in terms of "percent saturation." Percent saturation refers to how close the water is to holding its maximum amount at a given temperature. Rivers that have oxygen saturation levels between 90% and 110% are considered healthy. Water less than 90% saturated may contain large amounts of oxygen-demanding organic material. Water with over 110% saturation can result from excessive turbulence. The graph shown in Figure 1 is used to determine percent oxygen saturation based on the concentration of dissolved oxygen in ppm at a specific temperature. *Example:* Water containing 9.0 ppm DO at a temperature of 12 °C is about 80% saturated.

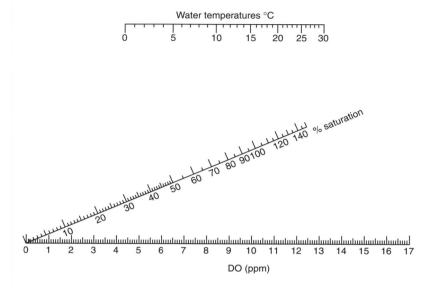

Figure 1. Percent Saturation as a Function of Temperature and DO Levels.

Dissolved oxygen levels depend on the amount of organic matter or waste in the water. (Organic waste is anything that was once part of a living plant or animal.) Organic waste can come from sewage, water treatment plants, urban and agricultural runoff, and discharge from paper mills, food processing plants, meat packing plants, or other industrial sources. When organic matter decays or decomposes, it is digested by aerobic bacteria, which use up dissolved oxygen in the process.

Biochemical oxygen demand (BOD) is a measure of how much dissolved oxygen (DO) is used by microorganisms in the aerobic oxidation of organic matter. BOD is determined by collecting two samples of water at the same time. The first sample is tested immediately to measure the initial DO level, while the second sample is incubated for 5 days in the dark to allow bacteria to decompose organic waste in the water. The difference between the initial DO level and the level remaining after 5 days is the BOD—the amount of oxygen consumed as a result of biological activity.

Dissolved oxygen (Day 1) – Dissolved oxygen (Day 5) = BOD (ppm)

Biochemical oxygen demand increases as water becomes more polluted. BOD levels of 1–2 ppm are healthy, while BOD levels greater than 3–5 ppm are indicative of poor water quality. Nitrate and phosphate pollution, for example, stimulates the growth of algae and other aquatic plants, leading to algae blooms. When the plants die, they are consumed by aerobic bacteria that deplete the level of dissolved oxygen and contribute to high BOD. High BOD conditions enable organisms that can tolerate low dissolved oxygen levels, such as carp, midge larvae, leeches, and sludge worms, to thrive. Organisms such as trout, salmon, and macroinvertebrates that are very sensitive to the amount of oxygen in water will not survive under high BOD conditions.

DO levels are proportional to pressure. See the Lab Hints *section for the pressure corrections. In most areas of the country, the pressure correction will be ±2–3%, which is probably within the accuracy or precision of the experiment.*

Teacher Notes

The amount of dissolved oxygen in water can be determined using a standard wet-chemical technique called the *Winkler method,* or by means of special dissolved oxygen sensors or meters. (The Winkler method is commonly used to calibrate or standardize dissolved oxygen sensors.) There are three basic steps in the Winkler procedure (Equations 1–3):

(1) Manganese sulfate and a basic potassium iodide solution are added to convert the dissolved oxygen to an insoluble manganese–oxygen complex. This step "fixes" the dissolved oxygen and prevents the oxygen from being consumed or reacting with other substances. Both the manganese sulfate and iodide solutions are added in excess to ensure that all of the oxygen has been sequestered. These solutions should be added *as soon as possible* (but no later than 24 hours) after a water sample has been collected in the field.

(2) Concentrated sulfuric acid is added to dissolve the manganese–oxygen complex, which then reacts with iodide ions to generate iodine.

(3) The iodine released in this reaction is titrated using a standard sodium thiosulfate solution with starch indicator (to make the endpoint more visible). When 20 mL of water is titrated with 0.0025 M sodium thiosulfate solution, the volume in mL of sodium thiosulfate added is exactly equal to the amount of dissolved oxygen in ppm.

$$Mn^{2+}(aq) \ + \ 2OH^-(aq) \ + \ \tfrac{1}{2}O_2(aq) \ \rightarrow \ \text{Oxygen–manganese complex}(s) \ + \ H_2O$$
Equation 1

$$\text{Oxygen–manganese complex}(s) \ + \ 4H^+(aq) \ + \ 2I^-(aq) \ \rightarrow \ I_2(aq) \ + \ Mn^{2+}(aq) \ + \ 2H_2O$$
Equation 2

$$I_2(aq) \ + \ 2Na_2S_2O_3(aq) \ \rightarrow \ Na_2S_4O_6(aq) \ + \ 2NaI(aq)$$
Equation 3

Experiment Overview

The purpose of this cooperative class project is to investigate the effects of various environmental factors on the amount of dissolved oxygen in water. Variables that may be studied include temperature, concentration of sodium chloride or other electrolytes, the presence of dissolved nutrients such as phosphates and nitrates, biochemical oxygen demand, and environmental water quality (field samples). Dissolved oxygen levels will be measured in the laboratory using the Winkler method. Water samples collected in the field may be analyzed using an oxygen sensor or pre-packaged reagents for dissolved oxygen testing.

Pre-Lab Questions

1. What is the general relationship between dissolved oxygen levels and water quality?

2. Consider the graph in Figure 1: What would be the range of dissolved oxygen values in ppm for water that is 90–110 percent saturated at 15 °C?

3. Determine the overall *mole ratio* for the reaction of oxygen with sodium thiosulfate in the Winkler titration: How many moles of sodium thiosulfate must be added in the titration for every mole of oxygen in the water sample?

4. Describe the criteria for a "fair test" procedure to study the effect of a single variable, e.g., nitrate levels, on the amount of dissolved oxygen in water.

The manganese–oxygen complex produced in step 1 of the Winkler procedure is variously described as $MnO(OH)_2$, MnO_2 or even $Mn(OH)_3$. The stoichiometry of the reaction requires that manganese is oxidized to the +4 oxidation state.

Materials

Distilled water, 100 mL

Sodium thiosulfate standard solution, $Na_2S_2O_3$, 0.0025 M, 30 mL

Starch indicator solution, 5%, 3 mL

Sulfuric acid (concentrated), H_2SO_4, 18 M, 3 mL

Winkler solution #1 (Manganese sulfate), $MnSO_4$, 3 mL

Winkler solution #2 (Potassium iodide and Sodium hydroxide), KI/NaOH, 3 mL

Erlenmeyer flask or bottle and rubber stopper to fit, 250-mL

Syringe (with optional "poor man's buret" stopcock), 10-mL

Beral-type pipets or dropper bottles, 3

Erlenmeyer flask, 125-mL

Graduated cylinder, 25-mL

Test tube, large, and rubber stopper to fit

Test tube rack

Disposable glass (Pasteur) pipet

Wash bottle

Thermometer

Safety Precautions

Sulfuric acid is extremely corrosive to eyes, skin, and other tissue. Winkler solution #2 contains sodium hydroxide and potassium iodide—it is a concentrated base solution and is caustic and severely corrosive. Concentrated sodium hydroxide solutions are especially dangerous to the eyes. Notify the teacher immediately in case of an acid or base spill. Wear chemical splash goggles, chemical-resistant apron, and chemical-resistant gloves. Avoid contact of all chemicals with eyes and skin and wash hands thoroughly with soap and water before leaving the lab.

Procedure

1. Add about 100 mL of distilled water to a 250-mL Erlenmeyer flask or plastic bottle. Stopper the flask and vigorously shake the flask 10–15 times to saturate the water with dissolved oxygen. Measure and record the temperature of the water.

2. Pour the water from the flask into a large (20 × 150 mm) test tube. Fill the test tube *completely,* all the way to the top, until the water just begins to overflow, and then immediately stopper the test tube. (Some water will be displaced. There should be no air bubbles trapped in the test tube.)

3. Remove the stopper and quickly add 6 drops of Winkler solution #1 (manganese sulfate solution) directly to the water in the test tube. Use a Beral-type pipet or a dropper bottle to add the solution, and hold the pipet or dropper as close to the water surface as possible.

4. Using a clean Beral-type pipet or dropper bottle, carefully add 6 drops of Winkler solution #2 in the same fashion. *Caution:* Winkler solution #2 is a concentrated base solution and is caustic and corrosive.

5. Stopper the test tube (some liquid will overflow), and carefully invert the stoppered test tube several times to mix the contents—a brown precipitate will quickly form. (This step fixes, or sequesters, the dissolved oxygen in the water. Fixed samples can be held up to 48 hours before they are analyzed by titration.)

Teacher Notes

6. Allow the brown precipitate formed in step 5 to settle to at least one-half the volume of the test tube (approximately 10–15 minutes).

7. Carefully add 6–7 drops of concentrated sulfuric acid using a disposable glass pipet. *Caution:* Concentrated sulfuric acid is extremely corrosive. Notify the teacher and clean up all spills immediately.

8. Replace the stopper in the test tube and invert several times to mix. The acid should cause the precipitate to dissolve, giving a clear amber (yellow–gold) solution.

9. Using a 25-mL graduated cylinder, pour 20.0 mL of treated water from the test tube into a 125-mL Erlenmeyer flask. (Use the top solution only—do not transfer any of the precipitate with the water.)

10. Fill the 10-mL syringe with 0.0025 M sodium thiosulfate solution and measure and record the initial (starting) volume.

11. Slowly add sodium thiosulfate solution from the syringe to the treated water in the flask until the water fades to a pale straw color.

12. Add 6 drops of starch solution to the treated water in the flask and swirl to mix. The sample will turn dark blue.

13. Continue adding the sodium thiosulfate solution dropwise to the water until the blue color fades completely. (This is the colorless endpoint.) Measure and record the final volume of sodium thiosulfate in the syringe.

14. Calculate the volume of sodium thiosulfate added and record the dissolved oxygen concentration in the data table. *Note:* For 20.0 mL of water, the milliliters (mL) of sodium thiosulfate added equals the dissolved oxygen concentration in parts per million (ppm).

15. *Cooperative class project:* Using the same general procedure, analyze the amount of dissolved oxygen in water (a) at different temperatures, e.g., 10 °C, 20 °C, and 30 °C; (b) for different concentrations of sodium chloride, e.g., 0.1 M versus 0.01 M; (c) for different amounts of water hardness, e.g., tap water or bottled soda water; (d) with different levels of nitrate contamination, e.g., 10 and 30 ppm of potassium nitrate.

16. *Field studies:* Collect water samples in the field and analyze using a dissolved oxygen meter or TesTab® tablets (follow the package directions). Fill a collection bottle or sampling container all the way to the top and cap immediately, taking care to avoid entrapping air bubbles in the container.

17. *Biological Oxygen Demand:* Collect two water samples in the field and analyze one sample immediately. Wrap the other sample container with aluminum foil and take it back to the lab. Store the container in the dark for five days before analyzing the DO again. (See the *Background* section.)

Name: _____

Class/Lab Period: _____

Dissolved Oxygen Testing

Data Table

Water Sample	Temperature	Sodium Thiosulfate (Initial Volume)	Sodium Thiosulfate (Final Volume)	Dissolved Oxygen Level
Distilled Water				

Post-Lab Questions *(Use a separate sheet of paper to answer the following questions.)*

1. Graph or analyze the class results for the effect of different variables, such as temperature or sodium chloride concentration, on the amount of dissolved oxygen in water.

2. Propose a simple explanation based on chemical or physical principles for why the solubility of oxygen and other gases in water decreases as the temperature is raised.

3. Nitrate pollution of surface waters due to fertilizer runoff is a serious concern in many agricultural and residential areas. Nitrate levels as low as 2 ppm may be harmful to amphibians and other forms of aquatic life, and levels >10 ppm are toxic to humans. How and why do high nitrate levels change the amount of dissolved oxygen in water?

4. The decomposition of decaying plant matter in water by aerobic bacteria is the reverse of the chemical reaction that occurs during photosynthesis. Write a balanced chemical equation for the consumption of oxygen when glucose ($C_6H_{12}O_6$) decomposes.

5. Explain why the amount of dissolved oxygen in a lake or stream increases during the day and then decreases at night.

6. How does biological oxygen demand influence the diversity of aquatic life?

7. How does the amount of oxygen dissolved in water (9–10 mg/L) compare with the amount of oxygen dissolved in air? Given that air contains 21 mole percent oxygen, calculate the concentration of oxygen in terms of milligrams of oxygen per liter of air at STP.

Teacher's Notes
Dissolved Oxygen Testing

Master Materials List *(for a class of 30 students working in pairs)**

Distilled water, 2 L

Sodium thiosulfate standard solution, $Na_2S_2O_3$, 0.0025 M, 500 mL

Starch indicator solution, 5%, 45 mL

Sulfuric acid (concentrated), H_2SO_4, 18 M, 45 mL

Winkler solution #1 (Manganese sulfate), $MnSO_4$, 50 mL

Winkler solution #2 (Potassium iodide and Sodium hydroxide), KI/NaOH, 50 mL

Erlenmeyer flasks or bottles and rubber stoppers to fit, 250-mL, 15

Syringes (with optional "poor man's buret" stopcock), 10-mL, 15

Beral-type pipets or dropper bottles, 45

Erlenmeyer flasks, 125-mL, 15

Graduated cylinders, 25-mL, 15

Test tubes, large, and rubber stoppers to fit, 15

Test tube racks, 15

Disposable glass (Pasteur) pipets, 15

Wash bottles, 15

Thermometers 15

*The listed amounts were calculated assuming that each pair of students will do three titrations—distilled water and two other solutions, such as 0.1 M and 0.01 M sodium chloride.

Preparation of Materials *(for a class of 30 students working in pairs)*

Winkler Solution #1: Pre-made solution may be purchased from Flinn Scientific (Catalog No. W0010). The solution contains 2.2 M manganese sulfate.

Winkler Solution #2: Pre-made solution may be purchased from Flinn Scientific (Catalog No. W0011). This solution has a fair to poor shelf life—use within one year of purchase. The solution contains 0.9 M potassium iodide in 12.5 M sodium hydroxide. It is caustic and corrosive.

Sodium Thiosulfate, 0.0025 M: Dissolve 0.62 g of reagent sodium thiosulfate pentahydrate ($Na_2S_2O_3 \cdot 5H_2O$) in approximately 500 mL of distilled or deionized water in a 1-L volumetric flask. Dilute to the 1-L mark with additional water. Prepare fresh within one week of use. The solution may be standardized by titration with potassium iodide/potassium iodate.

Starch Indicator Solution, 5%: Combine 5 grams of soluble starch with a few milliliters of distilled or deionized water and mix to a uniform paste. Add boiling water up to 100 mL. Cool to room temperature and refrigerate until ready to use. For best results, prepare fresh within one week of use.

Safety Precautions

Sulfuric acid is extremely corrosive to eyes, skin, and other tissue. Winkler solution #2 contains sodium hydroxide and potassium iodide—it is a concentrated base solution and is caustic and severely corrosive. Concentrated sodium hydroxide solutions are especially dangerous to the eyes. Keep sodium carbonate and citric acid on hand to clean up acid and base spills, respectively. Wear goggles or safety glasses whenever working with chemicals, heat or glassware in the laboratory. Please review current Material Safety Data Sheets for additional safety, handling, and disposal information. Remind students to wash hands thoroughly with soap and water before leaving the lab.

Disposal

Please consult your current *Flinn Scientific Catalog/Reference Manual* for general guidelines and specific procedures governing the disposal of laboratory waste. Tested samples and any unused sodium thiosulfate or starch indicator solution may be rinsed down the drain with plenty of excess water according to Flinn Suggested Disposal Method #26b. Winkler's solution #1 contains manganese sulfate and should be disposed of as heavy metal waste according to Flinn Suggested Disposal Method #27f. Winkler's solution #2 contains concentrated sodium hydroxide solution and may be neutralized for disposal according to Flinn Suggested Disposal Method #10.

Lab Hints

- The amount of time required for completion of this cooperative class project will depend on the number of variables that students will test in the lab and on the number of field studies that may be planned. In general, one 50-minute lab period should be scheduled for preliminary discussion and baseline analysis of distilled water at room temperature (to familiarize students with the Winkler titration method). Students can then use the time before the next scheduled lab period to plan an independent project (e.g., the effect of sodium chloride concentration on the amount of dissolved oxygen in water). Preparation and analysis of test solutions for the independent project can then be completed in a subsequent 50-minute lab period.

- The solubility of oxygen in water *decreases* as the temperature increases (this is true for all gases). The following table gives literature values for the maximum amount of oxygen in water as a function of temperature at standard atmospheric pressure. (The reference values are for water containing <0.1 g/L of sodium chloride).

Temperature	10 °C	12 °C	14 °C	20 °C	25 °C	29 °C
Dissolved Oxygen (ppm)	11.3	10.8	10.3	9.1	8.3	7.7

- The concentration of dissolved oxygen depends on pressure—the solubility of a gas *increases* as the partial pressure of the gas above the liquid increases. For most areas of the country, the pressure correction for the dissolved oxygen concentration will be small (±3%). To find the 100% saturation level at a pressure other than standard atmospheric pressure (1 atm or 760 mm Hg), multiply the literature value by the *ratio* of the barometric pressure to standard atmospheric pressure. *Example:* The solubility of oxygen in water at 20 °C and 740 mm Hg pressure is 8.9 ppm (9.1 ppm × 740/760).

- The small-scale titration procedure recommended in this activity gives accurate results (±3%) and is faster and easier to perform than a traditional titration. (In this activity, the water sample analyzed is 20 mL and the sodium thiosulfate concentration is 0.0025 M.) For larger water volumes (e.g., for field studies), multiply *both* the water volume and the sodium thiosulfate concentration by the same factor to keep the milliliters sodium thiosulfate added equal to parts per million of dissolved oxygen. *Example:* Use 0.025 M sodium thiosulfate solution to analyze 200 mL of water.

- *Field testing procedure:* Hold a 1-dram sample vial horizontally and gently lower it through the water surface to fill the container with water. Remove the overflowing sample vial from the water and add two TesTab® tablets. Cap the vial immediately, taking care not to entrap any air bubbles, and invert the sample vial until the tablets have dissolved. After 5 minutes, compare the color of the sample with the colors on the *Dissolved Oxygen Color Comparison Chart* to determine the ppm of oxygen. The color comparison chart is included with the purchase of TesTabs (Catalog No. AP5278).

Teaching Tip

- Analyze a pond, river or stream at several locations over the course of a year—in the spring after heavy rains, late in the summer following a prolonged hot, dry spell, during the cold winter months, etc. See the "Water Quality Index" activity in the *Demonstrations* section of this book for a discussion of how dissolved oxygen levels impact water quality.

Answers to Pre-Lab Questions *(Student answers will vary.)*

1. What is the general relationship between dissolved oxygen levels and water quality?

   In general, the amount of dissolved oxygen in water is highest when the water is clean and unpolluted. As the water quality declines, the DO level also decreases.

2. Consider the graph in Figure 1: What would be the range of dissolved oxygen values in ppm for water that is 90–110 percent saturated at 15 °C?

   The dissolved oxygen concentration will vary between 9.3 ppm (90% saturated) and 11.4 ppm (110% saturated) at 15 °C (59 °F).

3. Determine the overall *mole ratio* for the reaction of oxygen with sodium thiosulfate in the Winkler titration: How many moles of sodium thiosulfate must be added in the titration for every mole of oxygen in the water sample?

$$\frac{1 \text{ moles } O_2}{2 \text{ mole Mn–}O_2 \text{ complex}} \times \frac{1 \text{ mole Mn–}O_2 \text{ complex}}{1 \text{ mole } I_2} \times \frac{1 \text{ mole } I_2}{2 \text{ moles } Na_2S_2O_3} = \frac{1 \text{ mole } O_2}{4 \text{ moles } Na_2S_2O_3}$$

4. Describe the criteria for a "fair test" procedure to study the effect of a single variable, e.g., nitrate levels, on the amount of dissolved oxygen in water.

   In a fair test, all of the variables or conditions in the experiment, except for the dependent variable, should be held constant (controlled). At least two different values or levels of the dependent variable should be investigated, in addition to a control or baseline experiment. To test the effect of nitrate levels on dissolved oxygen, for example, at least two concentrations, such as 10 and 30 ppm nitrates, would be tested in addition to distilled water.

Sample Data

Student data will vary.

Data Table

Water Sample	Temperature	Sodium Thiosulfate (Initial Volume)	Sodium Thiosulfate (Final Volume)	Dissolved Oxygen Level
Distilled Water	21.6 °C	10.0 mL	1.5 mL	8.5 mg/L
	36.0 °C	10.0 mL	3.6 mL	6.4 mg/L
0.1 M NaCl	20.2 °C	10.0 mL	2.4 mL	7.6 mg/L
0.01 M NaCl	19.7 °C	10.0 mL	2.6 mL	7.4 mg/L

Answers to Post-Lab Questions *(Student answers will vary.)*

1. Graph or analyze the class results for the effect of different variables, such as temperature or sodium chloride concentration, on the amount of dissolved oxygen in water.

   The following graph shows literature data for the dissolved oxygen concentration as a function of temperature.

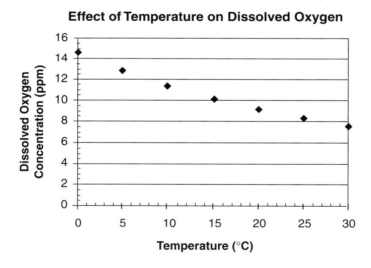

2. Propose a simple explanation based on physical principles for why the solubility of oxygen and other gases in water decreases as the temperature is raised.

   Note to teachers: *Accept all reasonable explanations—this is not an easy question! Most textbook explanations for the effect of temperature on the solubility of gases focus on the enthalpy of solution for oxygen in water and LeChâtelier's Principle. Dissolving oxygen in water is an exothermic process. According to LeChâtelier's principle, the solubility equilibrium for an exothermic reaction shifts back to reactants when the temperature increases. From a thermodynamic viewpoint, however, it makes sense to consider both the enthalpy and entropy contributions* to free energy (and hence the equilibrium constant). The entropy change for oxygen dissolving in water is negative. As the temperature increases, this process becomes less favored.

$$\Delta G = -RTlnK \qquad\qquad \Delta G = \Delta H - T\Delta S$$

As T increases, $-T\Delta S$ and ΔG both become more positive, so the value of the equilibrium constant K decreases.

3. Nitrate pollution of surface waters due to fertilizer runoff is a serious concern in many agricultural and residential areas. Nitrate levels as low as 2 ppm may be harmful to amphibians and other forms of aquatic life, and levels >10 ppm are toxic to humans. How and why do high nitrate levels change the amount of dissolved oxygen in water?

   Nitrate ions are a primary nutrient for the growth of plants and other forms of aquatic life. High concentrations of nitrate ions promote both plant growth and plant decay. As aquatic plants decay, aerobic bacteria consume the dissolved oxygen in the water faster than it can be replenished by photosynthesis.

4. The decomposition of decaying plant matter in water by aerobic bacteria is the reverse of the chemical reaction that occurs during photosynthesis. Write a balanced chemical equation for the consumption of oxygen when glucose ($C_6H_{12}O_6$) decomposes.

   $$C_6H_{12}O_6 + 6O_2 \rightarrow 6CO_2 + 6H_2O$$

5. Explain why the amount of dissolved oxygen in a lake or stream increases during the day and decreases at night.

   Oxygen is produced during the daylight hours as a result of photosynthesis by blue-green algae. At night, photosynthesis stops, but the respiration (metabolism) of all organisms continues. Respiration requires oxygen and thus depletes the oxygen dissolved in water until it can be replenished.

6. How does biological oxygen demand influence the diversity of aquatic life?

   *Aquatic life becomes **less diverse** as the biological oxygen demand increases. Organisms that will not tolerate low dissolved oxygen levels begin to die as the BOD increases, while a few organisms that are not as sensitive to DO will multiply and crowd out and overwhelm the others.*

7. How does the amount of oxygen dissolved in water (9–10 mg/L) compare with the amount of oxygen dissolved in air? Given that air contains 21 mole percent oxygen, calculate the concentration of oxygen (milligrams of oxygen per liter of air) at STP.

   At STP, one mole of air occupies an ideal gas volume of 22.4 L. There are 0.21 moles of oxygen, therefore, per 22.4 L of air.

   $$\frac{0.21\ moles\ O_2}{1\ mole\ air} \times \frac{32\ g\ O_2}{1\ mole\ O_2} \times \frac{1\ mole\ air}{22.4\ L\ air} = 0.30\ g\ O_2/L = 300\ mg\ O_2/L$$

Clearing Water with Alum
Water Purification

Introduction

Where does drinking water come from and how is it purified? In this demonstration, a commercial purification procedure for removing suspended solids from drinking water is introduced.

Concepts

- Coagulation and flocculation
- Water purification

Materials

Alum (Aluminum potassium sulfate), AlK(SO$_4$)$_2$·12H$_2$O, ¼ teaspoon, about 2 g

Ammonia, NH$_3$, 1 M, about 5 mL

Dirt, sand or soil, 2 tablespoons, 15–30 g*

Tap water

Beakers, 600-mL, 2

Measuring spoons or scoopula

Pipet, Beral-type

Stirring rod

Use garden soil, a mixture of soil and sand, or sand. If the water is particularly muddy, add more alum and ammonia. Different dirt or soil samples will require different conditions.

Safety Precautions

Ammonia vapor is extremely irritating to eyes and mucous membranes. It is also slightly toxic by ingestion and inhalation. Wear chemical splash goggles, chemical-resistant gloves, and a chemical resistant apron. Please consult current Material Safety Data Sheets for additional safety information.

Procedure

1. Fill two 600-mL beakers each with about 500 mL of water.

2. Add about ¼ teaspoon of alum to one beaker and stir until dissolved.

3. Add a tablespoon of dirt or sand to each beaker. Stir to make the water cloudy.

4. Add 2 pipets-ful of ammonia to the beaker containing the alum. Stir very gently once or twice. Once the ammonia is added, a white fluffy solid will begin to form around the suspended particles. The particles will coagulate and settle to the bottom of the liquid.

5. Compare the mixtures in the two beakers after 5 minutes and again after 30 minutes.

Disposal

Please consult your current *Flinn Scientific Catalog/Reference Manual* for general guidelines and specific procedures governing the disposal of laboratory waste. The waste liquids may be disposed of down the drain with plenty of water according to Flinn Suggested Disposal Method #26b. The dirt and flocculent material may be filtered and disposed in the trash according to Flinn Suggested Disposal Method #26a.

Before the demonstration, ask students where their drinking water comes from and how dirt and other solid particles are removed from drinking water. Many students are under the impression that some form of mechanical filtration such as a paper or metal strainer is used. These methods are impractical for filtering large volumes of water because of the propensity of the system to become clogged and thus restrict water flow.

Tips

- While waiting for the soil or sand to settle, discuss the commercial and consumer uses of alum. It is one of the earliest chemicals used by man. Alum is used as an astringent (a solution of alum on a wound will constrict the blood vessels and stop bleeding) and as an emetic to induce vomiting. One of the most important uses of alum is as a mordant or binder in dyeing. Alum binds to ionic and polar sites within a fabric and serves as a point of attachment to "fix" the dye molecules to the fabric.

- To test water for bacterial contamination, set up two beakers of the water samples that have been treated with alum. Add a few drops of ordinary household bleach (5.25% sodium hypochlorite) to the first beaker. Leave the second beaker untreated as a control. Allow the treated water to sit for half an hour. Using sterile technique, inoculate a few drops of each solution on nutrient agar plates or Petrifilm™. Quantitative results may be obtained using the "Bacterial Pollution (Coliform) Kit" available from Flinn Scientific (Catalog No. AB1152.)

Discussion

Many of the suspended particles in water are so small that their removal by filtration is not feasible. Most of these small particles are negatively charged. The negatively charged particles repel each other naturally and remain suspended in water. A process known as coagulation is used to help break up the suspended particles and destabilize the particle suspension . In this demonstration, coagulation is catalyzed using a chemical known as alum (aluminum potassium sulfate). Alum neutralizes the negative charges surrounding the small colloidal particles and allows the particles to coalesce and form clumps or "flocs" that will readily settle to the bottom of water.

In order for coagulation to occur using alum, a certain degree of alkalinity is required. When ammonia is added to the water, an optimum pH is obtained for the alum to react with the ions found in water to produce insoluble precipitates such as aluminum hydroxide $[Al(OH)_3]$ and calcium sulfate $(CaSO_4)$. See Equation 1. The insoluble, neutrally charged particles will then settle to the bottom of the liquid (Figure 1).

$$Al^{3+}(aq) + SO_4^{2-}(aq) + Ca^{2+}(aq) + 3HCO_3^-(aq) \rightarrow$$
$$Al(OH)_3(s) + CaSO_4(s) + 3CO_2(g) \qquad \textit{Equation 1}$$

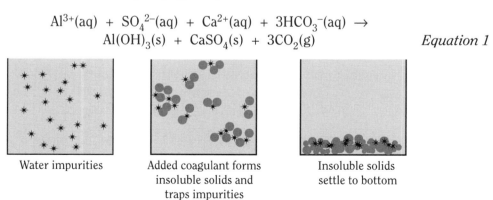

Water impurities

Added coagulant forms insoluble solids and traps impurities

Insoluble solids settle to bottom

Figure 1. Coagulation and Water Purification

Coagulation is generally followed by a slow-mixing technique known as flocculation, which promotes further aggregation of the coagulated particles. After coagulation and flocculation, the top layer of clean water will be siphoned off and treated with chlorine (commonly in the form of bleach) to kill bacteria.

Teacher Notes

Acid Rain in a Bag
Reaction of Nitrogen Oxides in the Atmosphere

Introduction

Perform a safe, microscale simulation of acid rain formation.

Concepts

- Oxidation–reduction
- Acid–base indicators
- Acid rain
- Environmental chemistry

Materials

Copper wire, 1 cm

Distilled or deionized water

Nitric acid, HNO_3, 6 M, 1 mL

Universal indicator solution, 4 mL

pH Paper (optional)

Pipets, Beral-type, 3

Overhead projector

Reaction plate, 24-well

Universal indicator color chart

Zipper-lock bag, 1-gallon size

Safety Precautions

Nitric acid is severely corrosive and a strong oxidizing agent. Nitrogen dioxide is a poisonous gas-do not inhale. Avoid contact of all chemicals with eyes and skin and perform this demonstration in a well-ventilated lab or in a fume hood. Wear chemical splash goggles, chemical-resistant gloves, and a chemical-resistant apron. Please review current Material Safety Data Sheets for additional safety, handling, and disposal information.

Procedure

1. Place a 1-cm piece of copper wire into one of the center wells of a 24-well reaction plate. Using a Beral-type pipet, place 1 mL of universal indicator solution into each of four corner wells of the 24-well reaction plate.

2. Fill each of the remaining wells with 1 mL of distilled or deionized water. *Note:* Do NOT add anything to the well containing the copper wire at this time.

3. Place the reaction plate into the zipper-lock bag and place the bag on the overhead projector.

4. Turn on the lamp on the overhead projector and focus the projector so the color of the universal indicator solution is visible. Observe and record the initial color of the universal indicator solution in the corner wells. *[The indicator is green, pH 7 (neutral).]*

5. Using a Beral-type pipet, carefully place about 16 drops of 6 M nitric acid into the well containing the copper wire. Quickly and cautiously zip up the bag so that no gases escape.

6. Observe the color changes of the universal indicator solution and the production of nitrogen dioxide, a brown gas, as nitric acid reacts with the copper. Relate the colors of the universal indicator solution to pH using the universal indicator color chart accompanying the indicator solution.

7. Within seconds, the nitric acid solution in the center well begins to bubble and a light blue-green color is visible. Within a few minutes, the universal indicator solutions in the corner wells turn yellow and then orange. The well closest to the nitric acid solution has some red streaks. A pale brown gas is visible directly above the center well.

8. *(Optional)* Use pH paper to test the pH of the distilled water in the wells at various distances from the center well. (The pH in the wells immediately adjacent to the copper wire/nitric acid mixture is 4–5, while the pH in the wells located diagonally across from the center well is 5–6.)

Disposal

Please consult your current *Flinn Scientific Catalog/Reference Manual* for general guidelines and specific procedures governing the disposal of laboratory waste. Rinse out the bag and dispose of the contents down the drain with plenty of excess water according to Flinn Suggested Disposal Method #26b.

Discussion

The burning of fossil fuels produces two major classes of air pollutants, nitrogen oxides and sulfur oxides. These gases react with water in the atmosphere to produce acid rain and other forms of acid deposition, such as acid fog, acid snow, and acid dew. Nitrogen and sulfur oxides are formed when oxygen reacts with sulfur or nitrogen. In the case of NO_x, nitrogen in the air itself combines with oxygen to form nitrogen oxides. Normally, atmospheric nitrogen and oxygen do not combine to form nitrogen oxides. (If they did, we would have a very acidic atmosphere, since our air contains 79% nitrogen and 21% oxygen.) However, at high temperatures, nitrogen and oxygen react much more readily to form NO_x. When automobile engines burn gasoline or when electric generating power plants burn fossil fuels (coal, oil or natural gas), the high temperatures of these combustion processes cause the nitrogen and oxygen in the air to combine to form NO_x.

This demonstration illustrates on a small scale the reactions of nitrogen dioxide in the atmosphere and its role in the formation of acid rain. Contact of copper metal with nitric acid results in a very rapid chemical reaction. The nitric acid is not only a strong acid but also a strong oxidizing agent. Copper is oxidized to copper(II) ions, and nitric acid is reduced to nitrogen dioxide gas in the process. Water is formed as a byproduct in this reaction. (See Equation 1.) The formation of dissolved copper(II) ions is evident from the blue color observed in the copper/nitric acid reaction well, while the nitrogen dioxide is visible as a brown gas.

$$Cu(s) + 4HNO_3(aq) \rightarrow Cu(NO_3)_2 (aq) + 2NO_2(g) + 2H_2O(l) \qquad Equation\ 1$$

The nitrogen dioxide gas produced in this reaction readily dissolves in water to give a very acidic solution (Equation 2). The effect of this acidic gas is observed almost immediately as the universal indicator solution in the outside wells begins to change color from green (neutral) to yellow and then orange (pH = 5–6) as the nitrogen dioxide dissolves in water and the pH falls.

$$2NO_2(g) + \tfrac{1}{2}O_2(g) + H_2O(l) \rightarrow 2HNO_3(aq) \qquad Equation\ 2$$

Buffering of Lakes and Streams
Acid Neutralization in Nature

Introduction

An "acid rainfall" solution is poured through a column of marble chips to illustrate the formation of a buffer in lakes with a limestone bed.

Concepts

- Acid rain
- Acid–base indicators
- Buffers
- Water quality

Materials

"Acid rainfall" solution
   (sulfuric acid, H_2SO_4, 0.1 M), 30 mL

Distilled or deionized water

Marble chips (Calcium carbonate, $CaCO_3$), 150 g

Universal indicator solution, 3 mL

Beakers, 250- and 400-mL, 1 each

Glass demonstration tube, 2 cm × 60 cm

Glass wool

Graduated cylinder, 10-mL

Pipets, Beral-type, or eyedroppers, 3

Ring (support) stand and buret clamp

Rubber stopper (2-hole) to fit tube, size 2

Stirring rod

Safety Precautions

Dilute nitric acid is solution is a corrosive liquid and irritating to eyes and skin. Dilute sulfuric acid solution is corrosive to eyes, skin, and other tissue—avoid contact of all chemicals with eyes and skin. Wear chemical splash goggles, a chemical resistant apron, and chemical-resistant gloves. Please consult current Material Safety Data Sheets for additional safety, handling, and disposal information.

Preparation

1. Place a tuft of glass wool loosely bunched up into one end of a long glass demonstration tube. Stopper this end of the demonstration tube with a two-hole rubber stopper.

2. Fill the glass demonstration tube about three-quarters full with marble chips.

3. Using a single buret clamp, attach the demonstration tube vertically to a support stand so that the stoppered end of the tube is at the bottom and the open end is at the top.

4. Place a 250-mL beaker under the stoppered end of the tube. Rinse the column of marble chips with tap water until the water leaving the column is clear (not cloudy), then rinse the column a second time with distilled or deionized water.

5. Discard the rinse water in the 250-mL beaker and clean the beaker before replacing it back under the column.

6. *Prepare the "acid rainfall" solution:* Fill a 400-mL beaker about two-thirds full with 250 mL of distilled or deionized water, and add 3 mL of universal indicator. Using a Beral-type pipet, add 1–2 drops of 0.1 M sulfuric acid or nitric acid to the indicator solution until it turns red (pH ≤4).

Procedure

1. Slowly pour the "acid rainfall" solution into the demonstration column filled with marble chips.

2. Observe and record the rainbow spectrum of color changes as the acid rain solution slowly filters through the column. *(As the acid rain filters through the column, it starts out reddish-orange at the top. After passing through about 2 cm of the column, the indicator solution turns orange, then yellow, green, and finally bluish lavender in sequence down the column.)*

3. Record the color of the filtrate after all of the acid rain solution has passed through the column. *(The filtrate is blue-green.)*

4. Using a Beral-type pipet, slowly add more acid rain solution to the filtrate in the beaker. Stir the filtrate with a stirring rod or using a magnetic stirrer. Observe the indicator color of the "naturally buffered lake" created in the beaker. *(The color of the filtrate remained dark blue even after 25 mL of the acid rainfall solution had been added.)*

Disposal

Please consult your current *Flinn Scientific Catalog/Reference Manual* for general guidelines and specific procedures governing the disposal of laboratory waste. The buffered filtrate and the dilute acidic rainfall solution may be rinsed down the drain with plenty of excess water according to Flinn Suggested Disposal Method #26b. The column filled with marble chips may be rinsed with distilled or deionized water and stored for reuse in future demonstrations.

Tips

• Fill parallel demonstration tubes with marble, granite, and sand and compare the effectiveness of different "soil types" in neutralizing acid rain. Test local soil samples to determine their buffering capacity as well.

• Bromcresol green may be used as an alternative acid-base indicator for this demonstration. Bromcresol green is yellow when the pH <3.8, blue when the pH > 5.4, and green in the intermediate or transition range between these two values. The color changes for bromcresol green occur at the lower pH limit for natural or normal rainfall. (Rain is naturally acidic, pH about 5.5, due to the presence of dissolved carbon dioxide from the atmosphere.)

• See "pH and Alkalinity of Water" in the *Experiments* section of this book for the quantitative analysis of the buffering capacity of natural water.

Discussion

The acidity of different bodies of water in a specific area can vary greatly. An increase in acidity is generally attributed to pollution in the form of acid rain or acid snow. Acid rain is precipitation that has absorbed and reacted with compounds (mainly sulfur oxides and nitrogen oxides) in the atmosphere. The term acid rain is generally used when the pH falls below pH 5.4. Given different bodies of water in the same relative area that are exposed to the same amount of acid rain, why do some bodies of water become more acidic than others?

Waters that are able to maintain a generally neutral pH do so largely because of the chemical makeup of the surrounding soil. Soils that are composed of carbonates, such as the marble chips (limestone) used in this demonstration, are able to neutralize acidic solutions. In contrast, soils that are composed mainly of silicates, such as sand or granite, have little or no acid-neutralizing capabilities. When acidic rainwater flows over soils high in carbonates, bicarbonate ions are produced and the rainwater runoff becomes more basic before entering a body of water. The majority of the lakes, rivers, and streams in the United States have pH values in the range of 6.5 to 8.2. As the pH of water drops below this range, several negative events may occur. The physiological processes within aquatic organisms can be disrupted or even disabled. Toxic metals are also chemically released readily in waters that have a low pH. The toxicity of the water may even reach a level where fish and other organisms can no longer survive.

Acid rainfall reacts with limestone (calcium carbonate, $CaCO_3$) to produce bicarbonate ions (HCO_3^-), see Equation 1. This reaction decreases the hydrogen ion concentration in the acidic rainfall and increases the pH, as evidenced by the spectrum of color changes for the universal indicator solution from red to orange to green as it percolates through the column in this demonstration.

$$H^+(aq) \; + \; CaCO_3(s) \; \rightarrow \; HCO_3^-(aq) \; + \; Ca^{2+}(aq) \qquad \textit{Equation 1}$$

The formation of bicarbonate ions sets up a natural buffer system whereby the "lake water" in the filtrate can resist the acidifying effect of additional acid rainfall (Equation 2). This reaction is evident from the resistance of the filtrate to change color when more acid rain is added to it.

$$HCO_3^-(aq) \; + \; H^+(aq) \; \rightarrow \; H_2CO_3(aq) \qquad \textit{Equation 2}$$

The existence of limestone in lake beds enables the lake to initially resist changes in pH when acid rain falls on the water. Moreover, the lake will continue to resist pH changes due to the formation of the buffer system.

Oil Spill Cleanup
Detergents, Dispersants, and Polymers

Introduction

Oil, oil everywhere! Considering the vast amounts of oil transported across the oceans throughout the world, oil spills are relatively rare. Cleaning up oil spills is nevertheless a major and recurring environmental challenge. How can science and technology help us solve the problems inherent in cleaning up an oil spill?

Concepts

- Oil spills
- Detergents and dispersants
- Absorbent polymers

Materials

Enviro-Bond™ 403 polymer, 20 g

Liquid detergent

Marvel Mystery Oil®, 30 mL

Tap water

Beaker, 600-mL

Cotton balls

Waxed paper or plastic wrap

Drinking straws

Feathers

Large glass bowl, crystallizing dish or beaker

Nylon stockings

Paper towels

Spoon, plastic

Safety Precautions

Marvel Mystery Oil® may be mildly irritating to eyes. It is a combustible liquid; keep away from heat and open flame. Enviro-Bond™ 403 dust may be irritating to eyes and mucous membranes. It is also slightly toxic by ingestion. Do not burn Enviro-Bond™ 403—the combustion products are toxic. Wear chemical splash goggles, a chemical resistant apron, and chemical-resistant gloves. Please consult current Material Safety Data Sheets for additional safety, handling, and disposal information.

Procedure

Part A. Modeling an Oil Spill

1. Partially fill a large glass bowl with water and pour a small amount (1–5 mL) of oil into the center of the pan to create an oil spill. Observe the initial appearance and properties of the oil spill.

2. Attempt to clean up the spill using cotton balls, paper towels, nylon stockings, and other materials. Record observations regarding the effectiveness of each material tested.

3. Using a drinking straw, gently blow across the surface of the spill to simulate windy or stormy conditions on the water surface. Retest selected materials under these "adverse weather" conditions.

4. Immerse a feather in the oil spill to model what happens to a seabird swimming or diving through a surface slick. Note the effects.

5. Add a small quantity of liquid detergent solution to the spill and observe what happens to the oil. Retest selected materials with the detergent added.

Part B. Cleaning up an Oil Spill

6. Fill a 600-mL beaker with 400 mL of tap water.

7. Add approximately 25 mL of Marvel Mystery Oil. The oil is less dense than the water and will form a thin layer on the surface of the water.

8. Add just enough of the Enviro-Bond 403 polymer to completely cover the oil. The polymer will immediately bond to the oil and will form a sponge-like mixture that floats on the surface of the water.

9. After 3–5 minutes, when all of the oil has been absorbed, remove the oil–polymer mixture with a plastic spoon and place it on a clean piece of waxed paper.

10. Notice how clean the water in the beaker looks—it is virtually crystal clear. As the polymer dries, it becomes firm and rubbery like sponge cake.

Disposal

Please consult your current *Flinn Scientific Catalog/Reference Manual* for general guidelines and specific procedures governing the disposal of laboratory waste. Enviro-Bond™ 403 and the gelled polymer may be disposed in the solid waste according to Flinn Suggested Disposal Method #26a. Recycle all oil waste—take used oil to an automotive service center, oil recycling station or authorized collection site.

Tips

- In Part A, challenge students to recommend possible spill cleanup materials and techniques based on their observations of the physical properties of oil and water. Let students experiment with a variety of other absorbent materials, such as sand, sawdust or different fabrics—use an open-ended, inquiry approach to stimulate creativity and imagination.

- Compare and contrast the relative effectiveness of the different materials that were tested. What did the most effective materials have in common? What did the least effective materials have in common? How would these methods translate into a larger, more realistic scale? What effect would weather have on the effectiveness of different techniques? (High winds and waves will inhibit cleanup efforts but may actually improve the actions of dispersants and hasten natural physical degradation.)

- Enviro-Bond 403 is a product of Petroleum Environmental Technologies, Inc., Rapid City, Michigan. Students may ask if the Enviro-Bond 403 will work on other types of oil such as vegetable oil. These oils do not have the necessary hydrocarbon components, namely the paraffin and the aromatics required to bond to the polymer.

- If Marvel Mystery Oil is not available, colored oils sold for use with decorative (kerosene) lamps will also work.

- Birds rely on air trapped in their layers of feathers to keep warm and buoyant. What effect does oil have on the feathers? What will happen to the bird under these circumstances? Have students investigate the short- and long-term effects of oil contamination on wildlife.

Discussion

Oil is a major source of groundwater contamination and ocean pollution. The vast majority of oil enters the ocean from oil spills on ships that transport petroleum or from manufacturing operations on land. However, oil can also seep into the ocean naturally from cracks in the sea floor.

On March 24, 1989, the Exxon Valdez ran aground on a rock reef in Alaska's Prince William Sound, spilling 11 million gallons (258,000 barrels) of crude oil. The magnitude and circumstances of the spill, questions about the timing and adequacy of the response, the pristine nature of the area, and the amount of coastline affected (more than 1200 linear miles) were all factors which combined to force this event into the minds of people worldwide. Much of the attention focused on the methods used to clean up oil both from the ocean surface and from affected beaches. The National Oceanic and Atmospheric Administration estimates that human cleanup efforts accounted for about 10% of the oil spilled from the Exxon Valdez. (The ultimate environmental fate of the remaining oil was accounted for by natural physical and biological processes.)

Some of the methods used to clean up oil spills include: (1) dispersants or detergents that break down the oil into small droplets that are more easily degraded; (2) booms, floating "sausages" with skirts that hang a few feet below the surface, which corral and contain the oil to facilitate mechanical removal; (3) skimmers, towed or self-propelled machines that collect the oil by skimming or vacuuming it from the surface; (4) hand scrubbing, blotting, or rinsing (with high pressure hoses) the oil from cobble or pebble beaches, and (5) enhanced biodegradation. Biodegradation is a naturally occurring process in which microorganisms effectively "digest" the spilled oil. Enhanced biodegradation (also called bioremediation) involves the application of nitrogen- and phosphorus-containing fertilizers to accelerate these natural processes.

Bioremediation techniques were applied on an unprecedented scale to treat the Exxon Valdez spill and appear to have been quite effective. Wildlife affected by the spilled oil was a magnet for a great deal of media attention, and mortality estimates varied widely. There is no question that everything from planktonic organisms to fish, seabirds, sea otters, bears, and eagles (from scavenging carcasses on the beach) were adversely affected. Among the most visibly affected were the sea otters and seabirds whose fur and feathers became coated and matted by the surface oil, leaving them prone to hypothermia, drowning, and absorption of toxins through their skin.

The oil stabilizing polymer called Enviro-Bond 403 is specially formulated to bond quickly and safely to many types of liquid hydrocarbons, including crude oil, diesel fuel, and gasoline. The bonding is so complete that the polymer literally encapsulates the liquid hydrocarbons in just minutes. Enviro-Bond 403 is a proprietary mixture of organic block copolymers that is specially formulated to absorb both aliphatic (paraffin) and aromatic hydrocarbons in petroleum.

Cleaning Up with Iron
Redox Reactions and Groundwater Remediation

Introduction

Since 1980, when Congress passed the first "Superfund" legislation to identify and clean up hazardous waste sites across the country, scientists and engineers have developed many innovative methods to remove contaminants from soil, surface water, and groundwater. Permeable reactive barriers (PRBs) are a good example of new technology that was created to solve environmental problems. A PRB is a wall built below ground to remove pollutants from contaminated groundwater. The walls are permeable, so water will flow through, but are made of reactive materials that will trap or detoxify pollutants. PRBs made of metallic iron are used to remove chlorinated organic solvents and heavy metals from groundwater. The chemical principle is simple—iron is a good reducing agent. It reduces toxic organic compounds and converts them to less harmful substances. The reaction of iron powder with organic redox indicators (dyes) demonstrates the "potential" of this method to reduce organic compounds.

Concepts

- Groundwater remediation
- Oxidation–reduction
- Permeable reactive barrier
- Chlorinated organic solvents

Materials

Distilled or deionized water

Indigo carmine dye, 0.25 g

Iron powder, 8 g

Methylene blue solution, 1%, 1 mL

Square-cut bottles, clear plastic, with caps, 60- or 125-mL, 2

Beral-type pipets, 2

Erlenmeyer flasks, 500-mL, 2

Spatula

Stirring rods, 2

Weighing dishes, 2

Safety Precautions

Iron powder and other metals in fine-powder form represent a possible fire and explosion risk. Keep away from flames, sparks, and other sources of ignition. Avoid breathing fine metal dust. Wear safety glasses or chemical splash goggles whenever working with chemicals, heat or glassware in the laboratory. Please review current Material Safety Data Sheets for additional safety, handling, and disposal information.

Preparation

1. Prepare 20 ppm methylene blue solution: Add 1 mL of 1% methylene blue indicator solution to 500 mL of distilled or deionized water in an Erlenmeyer flask or beaker. Stir the solution with a stirring rod to obtain a uniform concentration.

2. Prepare 20 ppm indigo carmine solution: Dissolve 0.25 g of indigo carmine in 100 mL of distilled or deionized water. Dilute 4 mL of this 0.25% solution to 500 mL with water to obtain a 20 ppm solution. For best results, prepare this solution fresh the day of use.

Procedure

1. Weigh approximately 2 g of iron powder into a small weighing dish. Using a funnel or weighing paper, transfer the iron into a clear plastic or glass bottle.

2. Pour the 20 ppm methylene blue solution into the bottle containing iron powder until the liquid is just about overflowing (try not to leave any air space or air bubbles in the liquid).

3. Cap the bottle and shake vigorously for 3–5 minutes. The bright blue dye solution will gradually fade and decolorize, and the resulting gray mixture will settle on standing to reveal a clear and colorless liquid and a bottom layer of iron.

4. The dye solution will remain colorless on standing for about 15 minutes before the blue color slowly begins to return due to air oxidation.

5. Follow a similar procedure to treat the 20 ppm indigo carmine solution, but use about 5 g of iron powder rather than 2 grams.

6. The indigo carmine solution will gradually change from its initial blue color to green and then to yellow. The mixture will settle on standing to give a clear yellow solution and a bottom layer of iron.

7. The dye solution will remain yellow for about 15 minutes before gradually turning green and then blue again. The first traces of green (oxidized color) appear near the cap, where air can enter, and then slowly diffuse throughout the liquid.

Disposal

Please consult your current *Flinn Scientific Catalog/Reference Manual* for general guidelines and specific procedures governing the disposal of laboratory waste. The heterogeneous reaction mixtures generated in this activity should be filtered to separate the iron powder. The waste iron may be packaged for solid waste disposal according to Flinn Suggested Disposal Method #26a. The remaining aqueous dye solutions may be disposed down the drain with plenty of excess water according to Flinn Suggested Disposal Method #26b.

Tips

- Permeable reactive barriers are a passive technology, relying on the natural flow of water underground to clean the groundwater. To illustrate the passive nature of PRBs, set up a series of capped test tubes containing methylene blue or indigo carmine solution. Add iron to the first test tube, and then add the same amount of iron to the next test tube in the series every day after that for five days. At the end of the week there will be a visible color gradient "from the ground up" in each test tube.

- Methylene blue and indigo carmine are used in classic demonstrations, the blue-bottle reaction and the "stop-and-go" light, respectively, to illustrate reversible oxidation–reduction reactions. Other redox indicators that give interesting color changes include resazurin and dichloroindophenol. The original (oxidized) colors of the dyes are restored upon standing (steps 4 and 7) because of reaction with oxygen in air.

Discussion

Permeable reactive barriers have been installed at more than 40 hazardous waste sites in the United States and Canada since 1980. PRBs are installed underground, beneath the water table, to clean up contaminated groundwater (Figure 1). A barrier is built by digging a long, narrow trench and installing the reactive material in the natural flow path of the polluted groundwater. PRBs do not require pumps or other expensive machinery, there are no

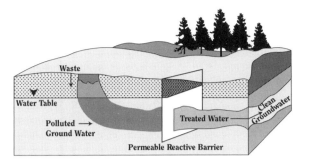

Figure 1. Installation and Design of a Permanent Reactive Barrier.

energy costs to operate the barriers, and the process does not generate additional waste that would need to be disposed of in a landfill or by incineration.

There are three major classes of PRBs. Barriers are designed to (1) trap pollutant chemicals by adsorption, using charcoal; (2) precipitate dissolved ionic pollutants using limestone; or (3) react with toxic chemicals and convert them into less harmful substances. Metallic (zerovalent) iron is the most important reactive chemical used in the third class of PRBs. Iron is inexpensive, readily available, and a good reducing agent, capable of reducing a wide range of organic and inorganic compounds in high oxidation states. So-called "iron walls" are commonly used to remediate groundwater contaminated with chlorinated organic solvents, such as trichloroethylene and perchloroethylene (dry-cleaning solvents), and are also effective for removing pesticides, nitrates, and chromates from water.

This demonstration illustrates the reduction of organic compounds using metallic iron. The substrates are organic redox indicators that exist in two oxidation states having different colors. The structures of the oxidized and reduced forms of the dyes are shown in Figure 2.

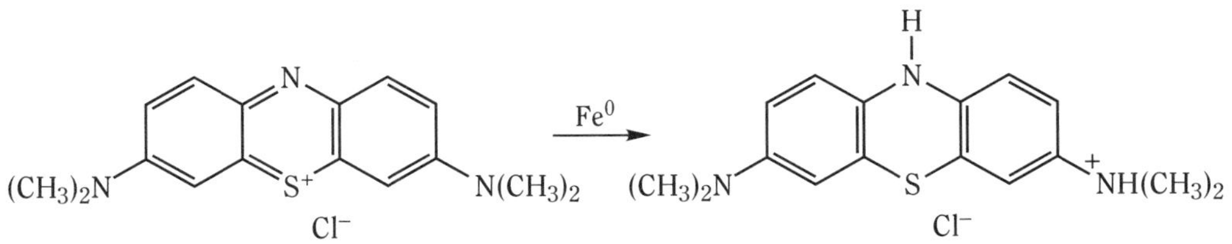

Oxidized Form (Blue)   *Reduced Form (Colorless)*

Methylene Blue

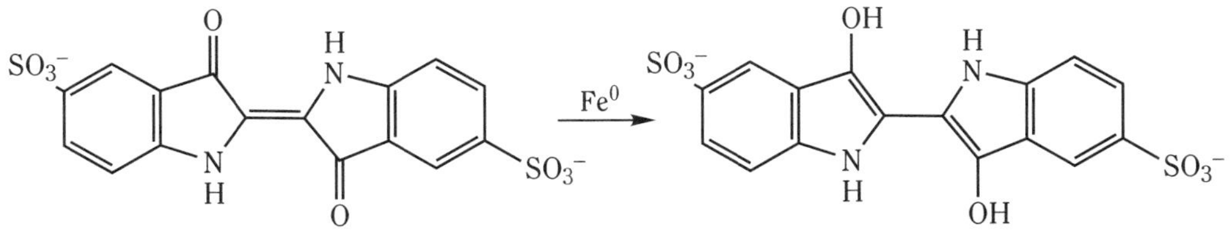

Oxidized Form (Blue)   *Reduced Form (Yellow)*

Indigo Carmine

Figure 2. Structures of Organic Redox Indicators.

Safety and Disposal Guidelines

Safety Guidelines

Teachers owe their students a duty of care to protect them from harm and to take reasonable precautions to prevent accidents from occurring. A teacher's duty of care includes the following:

- Supervising students in the classroom and laboratory at all times.

- Providing adequate instructions for students to perform the tasks required of them.

- Warning students of the possible dangers involved in performing the activity.

- Providing safe facilities and equipment for the performance of the activity.

- Maintaining laboratory equipment in proper working order.

Safety Contract

The first step in creating a safe laboratory environment is to develop a safety contract that describes the rules of the laboratory for your students. Before a student ever sets foot in a laboratory, the safety contract should be reviewed and then signed by the student and a parent or guardian. Please contact Flinn Scientific at 800-452-1261 or visit the Flinn Web site at www.flinnsci.com to request a free copy of the Flinn Scientific Safety Contract.

To fulfill your duty of care, observe the following guidelines:

1. **Be prepared.** Practice all experiments and demonstrations beforehand. Never perform a lab activity if you have not tested it, if you do not understand it, or if you do not have the resources to perform it safely.

2. **Set a good example.** The teacher is the most visible and important role model. Wear your safety goggles whenever you are working in the lab, even (or especially) when class is not in session. Students learn from your good example—whether you are preparing reagents, testing a procedure, or performing a demonstration.

3. **Maintain a safe lab environment.** Provide high-quality goggles that offer adequate protection and are comfortable to wear. Make sure there is proper safety equipment in the laboratory and that it is maintained in good working order. Inspect all safety equipment on a regular basis to ensure its readiness.

4. **Start with safety.** Incorporate safety into each laboratory exercise. Begin each lab period with a discussion of the properties of the chemicals or procedures used in the experiment and any special precautions—including goggle use—that must be observed. Pre-lab assignments are an ideal mechanism to ensure that students are prepared for lab and understand the safety precautions. Record all safety instructions in your lesson plan.

5. **Proper instruction.** Demonstrate new or unusual laboratory procedures before every activity. Instruct students on the safe way to handle chemicals, glassware, and equipment.

6. **Supervision.** Never leave students unattended—always provide adequate supervision. Work with school administrators to make sure that class size does not exceed the capacity of the room or your ability to maintain a safe lab environment. Be prepared and alert to what students are doing so that you can prevent accidents before they happen.

7. **Understand your resources.** Know yourself, your students, and your resources. Use discretion in choosing experiments and demonstrations that match your background and fit within the knowledge and skill level of your students and the resources of your classroom. You are the best judge of what will work or not. Do not perform any activities that you feel are unsafe, that you are uncomfortable performing, or that you do not have the proper equipment for.

Safety Precautions

Specific safety precautions have been written for every experiment and demonstration in this book. The safety information describes the hazardous nature of each chemical and the specific precautions that must be followed to avoid exposure or accidents. The safety section also alerts you to potential dangers in the procedure or techniques. Regardless of what lab program you use, it is important to maintain a library of current Material Safety Data Sheets for all chemicals in your inventory. Please consult current MSDS for additional safety, handling, and disposal information.

Disposal Procedures

The disposal procedures included in this book are based on the Suggested Laboratory Chemical Disposal Procedures found in the *Flinn Scientific Catalog/Reference Manual*. The disposal procedures are only suggestions—do not use these procedures without first consulting with your local government regulatory officials.

Many of the experiments and demonstrations produce small volumes of aqueous solutions that can be flushed down the drain with excess water. Do not use this procedure if your drains empty into groundwater through a septic system or into a storm sewer. Local regulations may be more strict on drain disposal than the practices suggested in this book and in the *Flinn Scientific Catalog/Reference Manual*. You must determine what types of disposal procedures are permitted in your area—contact your local authorities.

Any suggested disposal method that includes "discard in the trash" requires your active attention and involvement. Make sure that the material is no longer reactive, is placed in a suitable container (plastic bag or bottle), and is in accordance with local landfill regulations. Please do not inadvertently perform any extra "demonstrations" due to unpredictable chemical reactions occurring in your trash can. Think before you throw!

Finally, please read all the narratives before you attempt any Suggested Laboratory Chemical Disposal Procedure found in your current *Flinn Scientific Catalog/Reference Manual*.

Flinn Scientific is your most trusted and reliable source of reference, safety, and disposal information for all chemicals used in the high school science lab. To request a complimentary copy of the most recent *Flinn Scientific Catalog/Reference Manual,* call us at 800-452-1261 or visit our Web site at www.flinnsci.com.

Experiments and Demonstrations

Content Standards	Physical and Chemical Properties of Soil	pH and the Alkalinity of Water	How Hard Is Your Water?	Air Pollution Investigation	Build a Solar Cell	Dissolved Oxygen Testing	Clearing Water with Alum	Acid Rain in a Bag	Buffering of Lakes and Streams	Oil Spill Cleanup	Cleaning Up with Iron
Unifying Concepts and Processes											
Systems, order, and organization	✓	✓				✓		✓	✓		
Evidence, models, and explanation	✓			✓				✓	✓		✓
Constancy, change, and measurement	✓	✓	✓	✓	✓	✓					
Evolution and equilibrium											
Form and function					✓		✓			✓	
Science as Inquiry											
Identify questions and concepts that guide scientific investigation						✓				✓	
Design and conduct scientific investigations						✓					
Use technology and mathematics to improve scientific investigations		✓	✓		✓	✓					
Formulate and revise scientific explanations and models using logic and evidence	✓								✓	✓	✓
Recognize and analyze alternative explanations and models											
Communicate and defend a scientific argument											
Understand scientific inquiry				✓		✓				✓	
Physical Science											
Structure of atoms											
Structure and properties of matter	✓	✓			✓		✓	✓	✓	✓	✓
Chemical reactions	✓	✓	✓	✓	✓	✓		✓	✓		✓
Motions and forces											
Conservation of energy and the increase in disorder					✓						
Interactions of energy and matter				✓	✓						

Experiments and Demonstrations

Content Standards *(continued)*

	Physical and Chemical Properties of Soil	pH and the Alkalinity of Water	How Hard Is Your Water?	Air Pollution Investigation	Build a Solar Cell	Dissolved Oxygen Testing	Clearing Water with Alum	Acid Rain in a Bag	Buffering of Lakes and Streams	Oil Spill Cleanup	Cleaning Up with Iron
Science and Technology											
Identify a problem or design an opportunity						✓					
Propose designs and choose between alternative solutions											
Implement a proposed solution											
Evaluate the solution and its consequences											
Communicate the problem, process, and solution											
Understand science and technology					✓		✓			✓	✓
Science in Personal and Social Perspectives											
Personal and community health				✓							
Population growth											
Natural resources	✓	✓	✓	✓	✓	✓	✓	✓	✓	✓	✓
Environmental quality	✓	✓		✓		✓		✓	✓		
Natural and human-induced hazards	✓	✓		✓				✓		✓	✓
Science and technology in local, national, and global challenges					✓					✓	✓
History and Nature of Science											
Science as a human endeavor	✓	✓	✓	✓	✓	✓	✓			✓	✓
Nature of scientific knowledge	✓	✓	✓	✓		✓					
Historical perspectives	✓				✓					✓	

(for a class of 30 students working in pairs)   **Experiments and Demonstrations**

Chemicals	Flinn Scientific Catalog No.	Physical and Chemical Properties of Soil	pH and the Alkalinity of Water	How Hard Is Your Water?	Air Pollution Investigation	Build a Solar Cell	Dissolved Oxygen Testing	Clearing Water with Alum	Acid Rain in a Bag	Buffering of Lakes and Streams	Oil Spill Cleanup	Cleaning Up with Iron
Aluminum potassium sulfate	A0265							2 g				
Ammonium chloride	A0266			1 g								
Ammonium hydroxide (conc), 14.8 M	A0174			6 mL								
Ammonium hydroxide solution, 1 M	A0097							5 mL				
Bromthymol blue indicator solution, 0.04%	B0173				50 mL							
Calcium nitrate, tetrahydrate	C0349			1 g								
Calgon™	S0430	1 g										
Calmagite	C0002			1 g								
Copper, wire	C0148					1			1 cm			
EDTA, disodium salt, dihydrate	E0044			1 g								
Enviro-Bond™ 403	E0058										20 g	
Eosin Y	E0023	1 g										
Ethyl alcohol, 95%	E0009	500 mL										
Hydrochloric acid (conc), 12 M	H0031		9 mL									
Hydrochloric acid solution, 1 M	H0013				1 mL							
Indigo carmine	I0047											1 g
Iron, powder	I0013											8 g
Marble chips	M0032				30 g					150 g		
Marvel Mystery Oil®	AP8927										30 mL	
Methylene blue	M0072	1 g										
Methylene blue indicator solution, 1%	M0074											1 mL
Methyl orange indicator solution, 0.1%	M0078		50 mL									
Nitric acid solution, 6 M	N0048								1 mL			
Sand, fine	S0003	500 g						15 g				
Sodium thiosulfate, pentahydrate	S0114						1 g					
Starch, potato	S0122						5 g					
Sulfuric acid (conc), 18 M	S0228						45 mL					
Sulfuric acid solution, 0.1 M	S0419									1 mL		
Universal indicator solution	U0009								4 mL	2 mL		
Vinegar, white	V0005	20 mL										
Winkler's solution #1	W0010						50 mL					
Winkler's solution #2	W0011						50 mL					
Yeast, Baker's	Y0008				1							

(for a class of 30 students working in pairs)

Experiments and Demonstrations

	Flinn Scientific Catalog No.	Physical and Chemical Properties of Soil	pH and the Alkalinity of Water	How Hard Is Your Water?	Air Pollution Investigation	Build a Solar Cell	Dissolved Oxygen Testing	Clearing Water with Alum	Acid Rain in a Bag	Buffering of Lakes and Streams	Oil Spill Cleanup	Cleaning Up with Iron
Glassware												
Beakers												
50-mL	GP1005	42										
100-mL	GP1010		15									
150-mL	GP1015					2						
400-mL	GP1025		15							2		
600-mL	GP1030						2				1	
Burets, 25-mL	GP1089		15									
Culture dish, large	AB1265										1	
Erlenmeyer flasks												
125-mL	GP3040						15					
250-mL	GP3045		30				15					
500-mL	GP3050											2
Glass demonstration tube	GP9146								1			
Graduated cylinders												
10-mL	GP2005	7							1			
25-mL	GP2010						15					
100-mL	GP2020		15									
Pasteur pipets	GP7042						15					
Petri dishes	GP3019					8						
Stirring rods	GP5075					8			1	1		2
Test tubes												
16x125 mm	GP6065	35										
20x150 mm	GP6068						15					
20x150 mm, with caps	GP9158				15							
General Equipment and Miscellaneous												
Bottle, square, plastic, 60-mL	AP4527											2
Build A Solar Cell Kit*	AP6916					2						
Ceramic square	AP1245					2						
Clamp, buret, plain jaw	AP8354	28	15							1		
Cotton balls	FB0680										1	
Cotton swabs	AP1737					8						

*Build A Solar Cell Kit, AP6916 contains dried hibiscus, ethyl alcohol, iodine/potassium iodide electrolyte solution, nitric acid solution, titanium oxide, lens paper, tealight candle, binder clips, and electrical conducting glass.

(for a class of 30 students working in pairs)   **Experiments and Demonstrations**

General Equipment and Miscellaneous, continued	Flinn Scientific Catalog No.	Physical and Chemical Properties of Soil	pH and the Alkalinity of Water	How Hard Is Your Water?	Air Pollution Investigation	Build a Solar Cell	Dissolved Oxygen Testing	Clearing Water with Alum	Acid Rain in a Bag	Buffering of Lakes and Streams	Oil Spill Cleanup	Cleaning Up with Iron
Drinking straws	AP6025										1	
Forceps	AP8328					8						
Hot plate	AP4674					2						
Magnifying glass	AB1134				15							
Microscope slides, glass	ML1381				50	8						
Mortar and pestle	AP6066					2						
Multimeter	AP9000					2						
Nitrate in Water Test Kit*	AP6139	1										
pH test paper, narrow range, 3.0 to 5.5	AP325				1 roll			optional				
pH test paper, narrow range, 6.0 to 8.0	AP335		1 roll									
pH test paper, narrow range, 8.0 to 9.5	AP358		1 roll									
pH of Water Test Kit*	AP6141	1										
Phosphate in Water Test Kit*	AP6140	1										
Pipets, Beral-type, graduated	AP1721	35	15	30	45	24	45		1	3		2
Pipets, Beral-type, micrtip	AP1719			15								
Reaction plates, 24-well	AP1447			15	15				1			
Rubber stoppers, assorted sizes	AP2320	21					30					
Ruler, metric	AP1872	7			15							
Spatula	AP8338	14				8						1
Spoons, plastic	AP9285										1	
Support stand	AP8226	14	15							1		
Syringes, 3-mL	AP1728				15							
Syringes, 10-mL	AP1730				15		15					
Syringes, 60-mL	AP8754	28										
Test tube rack	AP1319	7					15					
Thermometers	AP6049						15					
Toothpicks, plastic	AP1810			75								
Tubing, plastic, 1/8 inch I.D.	AP8373				3 ft							
Vials, Snap-Seal™	FB0015	7										
Wash bottle	AP1668	7	15	15			15					
Weighing dishes	AP1278										2	

*Color comparison charts are included with Nitrate in Water Test Kit (AP6139), Phosphate in Water Test Kit (AP6140), and pH of Water Test Kit (AP6141)